GCSE Design & Technology for

Graphic products

Geoff Hancock • Keith Bolling

Series Editor: Geoff Hancock

www.heinemann.co.uk

✓ Free online support
✓ Useful weblinks
✓ 24 hour online ordering

01865 888058

Heinemann Educational Publishers
Halley Court, Jordan Hill, Oxford, OX2 8EJ
a division of Harcourt Education Limited
Heinemann is a registered trademark of Harcourt Education Limited

OXFORD MELBOURNE AUCKLAND
JOHANNESBURG BLANTYRE GABORONE
IBADAM PORTSMOUTH NH (USA) CHICAGO

First published 2005

10-digit ISBN: 0 435413 45 7
13-digit ISBN: 978 0 435413 45 3

09 08 07 06 05
10 9 8 7 6 5 4 3 2 1

Designed by Wild Apple Design
Produced by Kamae Design

Printed in Great Britain by CPI Bath

Index compiled by Ian D Crane

Illustrated by

Photographic acknowledgements
The authors and publisher should like to thank the following for permission to reproduce photographs:
Figures 1.1, 1.2 pp8 Trevor Clifford; 1.3 pp9 with kind permission of Nestle; 1.4,1.5 courtesy of Keith Bolling; 1.8 pp12 Gareth Boden; 1.11 pp14 Walkers Snacks Food Ltd; 1.12 pp 14 Arnos Design Ltd; 1.13 pp14 Encam; 2.46 pp35 International Olympics Committee (IOC); 2.54 pp38 Arnos Design Ltd; 2.55 pp38 Toblerone PR (Kraft Europe Office); 2.70-2.71 pp42 Arnos Design Ltd; 2.78 pp44 Trevor Clifford; 2.80 pp44 courtesy of Typhoo; 2.81 pp45 Arnos Design Ltd; 2.82 pp45 Trevor Clifford; 2.83 pp45 courtesy of The Virgin Group; 2.85 pp46 courtesy of Virgin Atlantic; 2.87 (a+b) pp47 Volkswagon; 2.88 pp47 Arnos Design Ltd; 2.89 pp48 IKEA; 2.90 pp48 Arnos Design Ltd; 2.92 pp 49 IKEA; 3.1 pp52 Aylesford Newsprint Ltd; 3.4 Arnos Design Ltd; 3.5 Arnos Design Ltd; 3.6 pp56 Arnos Design Ltd; 3.8 pp57 SWATCH; 3.9 pp57 Arnos Design Ltd; 3.11 pp59 David Churchill/Arcaid.co.uk; 3.12 pp59 The Badger Airbrush Company; 3.15 pp60 Arnos Design Ltd; 4.3 pp64 Peter Morris; 4.5 courtesy of SfE; 4.6 pp66 Peter Morris; 4.14 (a+b) Arnos Design Ltd; 4.20 (a+b+c) pp69; 4.26 pp72 Volkswagon; 4.28 pp72 Arnos Design Ltd; 4.30 pp73 Arnos Design Ltd; 4.31 pp73 Arnos Design Ltd; 4.35 pp74 © Cabaret Mechanical Theatre, web design by Gary Alexander; 4.36 pp75 reproduced with permission of Cadbury Limited; 5.1 pp78 Arnos Design Ltd; 5.12 pp84 GP Bowater/ALAMY; 5.13 pp85 London Transport; 5.17 pp87 Man Roland; 5.20, 5.21 pp88 Arnos Design Ltd; 6.1 pp96 Balearic Pictures/Alamy; 6.2 pp96 Corbis; 6.3 pp98 Magnum Photos/Bruno Barbey 1997; 6.4 pp99 NOKIA; 6.7 pp100 Joe Sohm/Alamy; 6.10 pp101 Wrapables.com; 6.13,6.14 pp102 Arnos Design; 6.15 pp103 Arnos Design Ltd; 6.16 pp103 Arnos Design Ltd; 7.1 pp106 Arnos Design Ltd; 7.2 pp106 reprinted with permission by HarperCollins Publishers Ltd © R.L.Stine; 7.3 pp107 courtesy of SfE; 7.8 pp108 Arnos Design Ltd; 7.9 pp108 Arnos Design Ltd; 7.10 pp109 Arnos Design Ltd; 7.11 pp109 Arnos Design Ltd; 7.13 pp109 Arnos Design; 7.14 pp110 Arnos Design Ltd; 7.15, 7.16 pp111 Harcourt Education Ltd,/Debbie Row; 7.23 pp114 Arnos Design Ltd; 7.24 pp115 Harcourt Education Ltd/Debbie Row; 7.25 pp115 Arnos Design Ltd; 7.28, 7.29 pp116 Arnos Design Ltd; 7.30 pp117 Man Roland; 7.35 pp118 Arnos Design Ltd; 7.36,7.37 pp119 Arnos Design Ltd; 7.39 pp121 Arnos Design Ltd; 7.43 pp122 Arnos Design Ltd; 7.45 reprinted with permission of HarperCollins; 7.47 pp125 reprinted courtesy of Constable Publishers; 7.48 pp124 ALAMY; 7.57,7.58 pp127 courtesy of Keith Bolling; 7.64,7.65 pp130 KitKat Bar with kind permission of Nestle; Figure 7.66 pp131 with kind permission of Nestle; 7.67 pp132 Arnos Design Ltd; 7.68 pp133 Toblerone PR (Kraft Europe Office); 7.71 pp134 Harcourt Education Ltd; 8.6 pp142 Harcourt Education Ltd/Tufor Photography;

Cover photograph by Getty/Brand X
Cover design by Wooden Ark

Picture research by Helen Reilly and Natalie Gray

The publisher would like to thank the following for permission to reproduce copyright material:
AQA material is reproduced by permission of the Assessment and Qualification Alliance.

Where sample answer and examiners' comments have been provided, these are the responsibilty of the author and have not been provided or approved by AQA. A special thanks to the students who allowed their coursework to be reproduced in this publication.

The publishers have made every effort to trace copyright holders. However, if any material has been incorrectly acknowledged, we would be please to correct this at the earliest opportunity.

Contents

Introduction

This book has been written to meet the requirements of the full and short course AQA specifications for GCSE Graphic Products. The AQA specification is designed to meet the National Curriculum Orders and GCSE subject criteria for Design and Technology.

The programme of study for Design and Technology at Key Stage 4 requires you to develop your design and technology capability by applying knowledge and understanding of graphic products when developing ideas, planning, making products and evaluating them. This book has given particular emphasis to the newer elements within the specification, such as industrial practices, ICT, CAD/CAM, and new and smart materials.

AQA specification

The specification provides opportunities for you to develop design and technology capability throughout your course. It requires you to combine skills with knowledge and understanding in order to design and make quality products in quantity. It also provides opportunities for you to acquire and apply knowledge, skills and understanding through:

★ analysing and evaluating existing products and industrial processes
★ undertaking focused practical tasks to develop and demonstrate techniques
★ working out how to develop ideas, and plan and produce products
★ considering how past and present design and technology affects society
★ recognising the moral, cultural and environmental issues in design and technology situations
★ using ICT.

How will you be assessed?

You will be assessed in two ways. You will complete a coursework project making up 60% of your GCSE mark. You will also complete a 2-hour (1-hour for the short course) written exam at the end of the course that will make up 40% of your GCSE mark. In both the coursework and the written exam, you will be assessed on how you demonstrate your knowledge, skills and understanding in three ways:

★ of materials, components, processes, techniques and industrial practice (20%)
★ when designing and making quality products in quantity (60%)

★ when evaluating processes and products and examining the wider effects of design and technology on society (20%).

Most of your marks (60%) will be awarded for designing and making. Most of your designing and making will be completed in your coursework project.

How to use this book

This book will help you:
★ develop your graphic skills
★ develop your knowledge and understanding of graphics and all the related topics required within the AQA specification
★ understand what is required for internal assessment (coursework) and how to get the best grades
★ prepare for and revise the written exam and understand how to get the best grades
★ develop key skills of communication, application of number, information and communication technology, working with others, problem solving and improving your own learning through your graphic products work.

This book is divided into the following parts:
★ Part 1 What you need to know: this is the main part of the book and contains sections 1–7
★ Part 2 Doing your coursework project: this contains section 8 and gives advice on how to plan and produce your coursework, helping you to get the best marks possible
★ Part 3 Preparing for the exam: this comprises section 9 and gives advice on what examiners are looking for, how to prepare for the exam and how to get the best marks you can.

Part 1 is written in double-page chapters. Each chapter includes:
★ specification links to show which modules of the AQA specification are covered by the chapter
★ a link to the relevant coursework assessment criteria covered by the chapter
★ an introduction showing what you will learn from the chapter
★ activities that reinforce and develop learning
★ a summary of the chapter to help with revision.

Chapters that include an activity involving the use of ICT are identified by the ICT icon **ICT** at the top of the page.

AQA Graphic Products 10.5 and 10.6

Numbering is used on each double-paged chapter to show which section of the AQA Graphic Products specification the chapter matches.

D1 Some chapters of Part 1 are also useful for the coursework project. This is identified by showing the relevant coursework assessment criteria at the top of the chapter. Here, 'D' refers to Designing and 'M' refers to Making. Along with the numbering, these are taken from the coursework project assessment criteria given in section 16.3 of the AQA specification. Please note that grades F and G have fewer assessment criteria, so the numbering here is based on grades A–E for consistency.

Some chapters might also include:

★ coursework boxes: these show how particular chapters in Part 1 are relevant to your coursework, so you should keep this information in mind when completing your project. You will also need to make sure you read Part 2 so that you understand exactly what you need to do for your project

★ case studies: these give real examples of how the processes and knowledge you are learning are applied in real life.

At the end of each section in Part 1 there are relevant examples of exam questions and the marks available. These will help you to practise and revise for the exam.

Finally, there is also a glossary at the end of the book to explain words identified in bold text. This will be useful as you are going through your course and also when you come to revise for the exam or do your coursework.

Websites

There are links to relevant websites in this book. In order to ensure that the links are up to date, that the links work, and that the sites are not inadvertently linked to sites that could be considered offensive, we have made the links available on the Heinemann website at www.heinemann.co.uk/hotlinks. When you access the site, the express code is 3457P.

Short course

If you are following the short course, you will need to use just some of the chapters in this book. You will need guidance from your teacher on how to use this book and which chapters to use.

This section focuses on the main elements of designing needed for success in your coursework. Important research techniques such as product analysis are explained, along with techniques to test and evaluate the effectiveness of a product.

What's in this section?

Product analysis

Learning from products

Looking carefully at products that are similar to the one you are designing is an important part of the design process. To learn successfully from existing products, you have to look at them with a critical eye. Looking critically at products and asking questions about them is known as product analysis.

Analysing graphic products

When you analyse a graphic product, you should always use the 5WH approach. This means asking who, what, where, why, when and how. This will act as a good starting point.

A **point-of-sale display (POSD)** is a graphic product so, for example, if you were analysing the POSD in the photo below, you might ask the following questions.

A point-of-sale display

Who is the product aimed at?

To answer this question, you have to think of the type of product it is promoting. For example, soap powder is usually aimed at adults. Look to see if there are any visual clues. A visual clue is anything that helps you to understand what the **designer**'s intentions are. It may be a picture, a style of writing or a particular choice of colours. For example, the visual clues in the POSD below are the use of pictures with children's characters, together with bright colours and large lettering.

What is the purpose of a point-of-sale display?

A display has to hold leaflets, but how many? Does the number of leaflets it needs to hold affect its size? Leaflets are usually made to a standard paper size, which could be A4, A5 or even A6.

Holding leaflets is probably the primary function of a POSD. It also has the secondary functions of attracting attention to the product being advertised on the leaflets and helping to sell it.

What material has been used and why?

Cardboard has been used to make the POSD below. This is the material of choice for virtually all POSDs. This is because:
- it is cheaper than thin plastic – this is important because usually the POSD has to last only as long as the product promotion

Cardboard is relatively strong and stable and provides a rigid structure when assembled

- it provides a good printing surface, particularly if a **bleached** white surface board is used
- it can be folded flat for delivery – this is important for transportation and storage.

Graphic products are often ephemeral

Ephemeral graphic products are things, like tickets and posters, which are designed to last for a short period of time and then be thrown away. One of the important questions for you to ask is, how does the fact that many graphic products are short-lived affect their design and manufacture?

Comparing graphic products

Sometimes it is useful to compare graphic products to find out why similar products have been designed differently. This type of analysis is called comparative analysis. There are hundreds of types of chocolate bars that are all more or less the same and which have the same function. However, their wrappers have been designed differently to reflect the different types of customers, their age groups and tastes.

Questions that need to be asked when carrying out comparative analysis of a range of similar products are as follows:

- Why are different colours used? Red is commonly used because it is aggressive and stands out. Think about why other colours are used.
- Why do products aimed at children look different from products designed for teenagers or adults? Thinking about this question will help you to understand different markets. A market generally refers to the type of people who use a certain product.
- Why do products have different types of packaging and use different materials? Thinking about this question will help you to understand production and packaging techniques, and why some products have to be completely sealed.

The same basic product has been designed differently. This is called product differentiation and is used to meet the needs of differing consumer tastes

Coursework

The ability to learn from different products is an important skill that you will use as part of the research section of your coursework project.

Activity

Collect examples of chocolate wrappers or use the photo above to carry out a comparative analysis. Try to think of reasons why the designers have made them differently.

Summary

★ Looking critically at products and asking questions about them is known as product analysis.

★ Carrying out comparative analysis helps you to draw conclusions about the designers' intentions and the techniques used to achieve product differentiation.

Designing

Modelling

Designers use 3D models of their designs to help communicate more clearly what the product looks like and how it might be used. A model can be classified as a representation of a real product but may differ in some important ways: the model may have no working parts and will be made to a smaller scale.

At GCSE-level, you may manufacture working products such as leaflets and point-of-sale displays, but you can also make scale models as part of your coursework. Typical scale models made by GCSE students are shown below.

A card model of a point-of-sale display

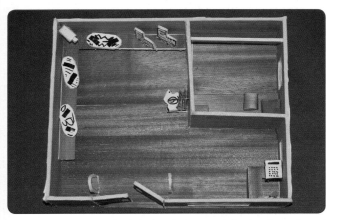

An interior design model using foam board

Modelling materials

Before any modelling takes place, a designer needs to find out what materials are available.

Sheet materials

Paper, card and thin plastic sheet are excellent for developing initial ideas as well as fully formed presentation models. A realistic model can be made, which is cheap and easy to cut and shape. Sheet materials can be manipulated as follows:

• **Laminating**: adding layers of card on top of each other to create a 3D form.
• Foam board (foam sandwiched between two thin sheets of card) is good for creating architectural models and interiors.

Moulding materials

Pliable materials like Plasticine and clay are good for creating a solid form like a computer mouse. Many designers use clay for adding subtle surface features that would otherwise be difficult to produce. Plasticine is best used for small models. Hard wax is good for producing a 3D form when machined using a **CNC** mill. A **CAD** drawing of an object can be downloaded into the machine, which then cuts out the object.

Block materials

The main material used in graphic products is polystyrene foam (Styrofoam). This is available in sheets of various thickness and can be cut and shaped easily into complex shapes. In general, Styrofoam can be cut using most woodworking and standard modelling tools. If block-type products are being made, it is sometimes best to cut the Styrofoam into pre-shaped blocks (slabs) before gluing them together.

The slab method also helps to show **mould** lines in products, or where a product is assembled from more than one part, such as the battery compartment of a mobile phone. Use a sharp knife to carve carefully in grooves to show these features.

Tool	Uses/tips
Scissors	Cutting paper, thin card and thin plastic. Ensure scissors are strong enough and use safely
Scalpel	Cutting thin card, plastic and balsa wood. Must be used with a safety rule when making straight cuts
Craft knife	As above, but heavier-duty card can be cut. When cutting card, always cut from an internal corner to the outside. On Styrofoam, use light force to prevent tearing
Rotary cutter	Cutting circular shapes in card or paper. Best for large curves and completion in one operation only
Trimmer	Cutting paper, thin card and thin plastic. Use the guidelines on the trimmer to ensure accuracy
Safety rule	Helps to make cutting straight lines easier with a sharp knife. Press down firmly with one hand on the rule while cutting
Scoring tool	Making indentations in card prior to folding. If a specialist tool is not available, use an old ballpoint pen – do not score with a knife as this weakens the material
Sandpaper block	Used for smoothing and shaping Styrofoam models. Use appropriate grades to get the best finish – light strokes are required otherwise the foam will tear
Glue spreader	Useful not just for spreading glue but for applying filler to a model

Modelling tools

Modelling tools

Once a designer has chosen a suitable material to work with, they then need to select the appropriate tools to do the modelling. (See the table above)

Scale

Most models are made to a suitable scale depending on the size of the real object:
- Very small objects: 2:1 (twice full size).
- Handheld objects: 1:1 (same size).
- A piece of furniture: 1:10.
- A room interior: 1:25.
- A house or garden: 1:100.

The most important thing to remember is that the size of the model should be able to show the main details while still being manageable to make.

Surface finishing

Some modelling materials require fillers to create a more even surface texture. Once a surface has been sanded down and is smooth, a range of finishes is available:

- sanding sealer
- primer (used as a base coat)
- cellulose paint

Coursework

Think carefully about what aspects of your design you need to present through a model – experiment with different materials and finishes and show this in your design development.

Activity

What scale would it be best to use for the following?
a A chair.
b A shop interior.
c A mobile phone.

Summary

★ Modelling is used to communicate what a product looks like in 3D.

★ There are various materials to choose from. You need to think about the design and purpose of your model before selecting the most appropriate one.

★ The correct scale should be used when modelling different-sized objects.

★ Foam materials need a filler to give a smooth surface finish.

Designing

Testing and evaluation

In this chapter you will:
★ **learn why evaluation is important and how it contributes to successful designing**
★ **learn the difference between formative evaluations and summative evaluations.**

Testing

Testing a design solution is an important part of the design process. Before any products are manufactured, they must undergo a series of tests.

Physical tests

Physical tests are carried out to ensure that the **design idea** works according to the **specification**. For example, a point-of-sale display leaflet dispenser will be tested to ensure that:
- it holds securely the correct number of leaflets
- it is stable (it does not tip over easily)
- it is strong and rigid.

A point-of-sale leaflet holder

Consumer tests

In addition to physically testing models, it is important to find out what potential users (consumers) feel about the product. Consumer tests are carried out on a sample of people within the identified target market for the product to find out their reaction to the design. These tests can take the form of a **questionnaire** or a simple ranking test. Ranking tests – sometimes referred to as preference tests – require users to state which product they prefer from a range. This helps designers to improve the appearance of the product.

Evaluation

Evaluation means critically asking questions about how well design ideas or the final product meets the design specification. The evaluation is not just something that occurs right at the end of a project; the best coursework has evaluation at various stages all the way through the process. This is because there are two types of evaluation:
- formative evaluation
- summative evaluation.

Formative evaluation

Formative evaluation is ongoing and takes place every time you make a decision or judgement about your work. The judgements you make should be in relation to the design specification. That is why a detailed design specification is so important to success at GCSE.

Summative evaluation

Summative evaluation occurs at the end of the project. It judges specifically how well the final 'made' product meets the design specification. It should include proposals for further development of the product or improvements to the manufacturing system to improve quality. For good evaluations:
- answer every point on the design specification
- write in the third person (never say things like 'I think...')
- include **sketches** of how to improve the product
- include the opinion of someone other than you – ideally the client or a member of the product's target market.

Coursework

When writing evaluations in your coursework, do not write a diary of how you got on or give opinions that you cannot prove by testing.

EVALUATION

Now that I have made my point of sale display, I can evaluate both its ability to meet my initial design specification, and its generally quality. To give me a few short indications into the quality of my product, and its ability to meet my specification, I carried out a few short tests on my completed point of sale Display. These were:- A weight test, a wind test (stability), and my User Trial, which will help me to evaluate and hypothetically suggest improvements to reproduce my point of sale Display.

The weight test I conducted was to see if my point of sale Display could hold 2 cd's, it managed this function well as you can see from the picture. This means it met its function in as much as it has the ability to hold CD's, a point of my design specification. For the stability test, I gave the point of sale display a quick burst of air from my hoover, this would be the equivalent of a reasonably strong gust of wind, which may blow through a shop. The point of sale Display remained standing after this, which suggests to me that the stand is very stable and durable. Of course, the product wouldn't be prone to adverse weather conditions, as it is at the counter in a shop, but a swift walking customer would pose a similar gust of wind to

challenge the stability of my point of sale Display, and this test is shown in this picture.

The user trial which I conducted, is documented on the previous page, and from it a number of suggestions have been made to improve my point of sale Display These are - that my stand was either good or excellent in the following areas- readability, influence over the consumer, colour scheme, accessibility (ergonomic association), attractiveness and general quality. It was suggested that to improve it, I could include some sort of interactivity. They said I could also include more white text, and more prominent white text. These suggestions, whilst also being peoples opinions would be key in the reconstruction of my point of sale display as these are the opinions of my consumer target market, and thus if they're needs are met more fully the sales of the promoted product would increase and inturn my products ability to meet its function would increase. I can also now evaluate how well my product met my design specification, by adressing the point of sale Displays ability to meet the function: My function was to increase sales of my chosen album by effective promotion, I feel my stand attracts consumers adorably, and can conclude from my user trial that my point of sale Display is very good in influencing consumers to buy my product.

Evaluation of initial research helps you to make decisions about your choice of material. Key aspects of the design such as the appearance and function should be judged against how well they meet the requirements of the design specification

This final evaluation looks back at the design specification and judges how successful the product is in relation to the original intentions

Activities

1 What is the difference between formative and summative evaluations?

2 In which three stages of the design process might you expect to see clear evaluation from a student?

3 What is the significance of the design specification to the summative evaluation?

Summary

★ Testing is an important part of the design process because it helps the designer to evaluate the strengths and weaknesses of a design idea.

★ A final (summative) evaluation needs to use the design specification as a checklist to make sure the designed product completely satisfies all design requirements.

Designing

Exam questions

1 The photo below shows a potato crisp packet.

a Name two important design features of the crisp packet. *(2 marks)*

b State two important properties that the material used for the crisp packet should have. *(2 marks)*

2 Symbols A and B below are two symbols often used on food and drink packaging.

Symbol A

Symbol B

a State the meaning of symbol A. *(2 marks)*

b State the meaning of symbol B. *(2 marks)*

c Write a short evaluation of the effectiveness of symbols A and B shown above. *(6 marks)*

Design skills

This section covers the techniques, processes and subject knowledge required to help you create effective design solutions for both your coursework and the final exam. It is important to develop your own graphical skills so that you can communicate ideas using a variety of methods and media. Remember that you will be graded not only on the level of skill you show but also on how you use and apply the knowledge you have learnt in communicating your design proposals to another person.

It is recommended that you practise the skills described in this section throughout the whole GCSE course so that you become confident in your own ability.

What's in this section?

2D and 3D sketching

In this chapter you will:

★ learn how 2D and 3D sketching are important techniques and can be used to communicate ideas.

Comparing 2D and 3D sketching

Freehand sketching

Sketching is a vital skill all designers need to master. Informal, ruler-free drawings are used as part of visual thinking and development. This is not only useful for the designer's benefit, but also when showing designs to others for discussion.

If you visit any design studio, you will see ideas sketched on backs of envelopes, scraps of paper – indeed, any handy surface. When an idea comes, formal drawings take too long and the idea could be lost. With this in mind, freehand sketching should not use rulers or any other drawing aids as these slow down the process.

Sketches can be created using pencils, ink pens or spirit markers. Experiment with different graphic media to develop your own sketching style.

The most important thing to remember is not to be afraid of making mistakes. Sketch boldly and confidently and try not to cover up errors by erasing or scrapping a page. All ideas, however rough in form, are an important part of communicating what you are thinking.

An object in 2D and 3D

2D and 3D sketching

2D sketching is the most basic form of drawing and the easiest to do. Drawing an object in 2D means drawing it in two dimensions – length and height or width – which means only being able to see one face of the object. This method has limitations in this respect, but it is a good starting point and most 2D ideas can be converted quickly into 3D.

A 3D drawing shows an object in three dimensions – length, height and width. These sketches show more information and make your ideas look more solid and realistic.

Crating

Drawing boxes or 'crates' is a useful method for creating a 3D sketch or drawing. Try to imagine the object you want to draw is inside a 3D box. Draw the box faintly and then draw the object inside, using the box (crate) as a guide.

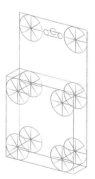

The stages in drawing an object using a crate

Once this technique has been mastered, it is surprising what you will be able to draw convincingly. Try to develop a free-flowing style and practise drawing simple objects to gain confidence.

Using grids and underlays

Graphic designers often want to produce more accurate sketches and insert a grid underneath their sheet of paper to help them. These are available in different forms:

- Square grids: these are useful for 2D drawings and enable you to follow the lines on the grid to get the scale and proportion of the drawing correct. They are also good for producing orthographic projections (see pages 28 and 29).

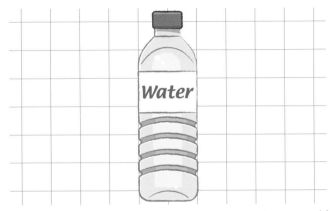

A square grid

- Isometric grids: these consist of lines at 30° to the horizontal, together with vertical lines. These grids can be created on a computer CAD package and printed out, which is helpful because you can vary the size of the grid pattern. Pre-printed grids can also be purchased. Drawing with them is easy once the basic principle has been mastered.

An isometric grid

Proportion

Designers sometimes say, 'If it looks right, it is right.' Although not always the case, it tends to be correct when applied to drawing. Proportion is the relationship between the sizes of objects or parts of an object to each other. Some objects look unbalanced if one part is too big or too small. There are 'rules' in the natural world that give living things proportion. Take the human figure, for example. If a ratio is taken from the height of a person to their navel, it will almost always fall near to 1.6. This ratio is often called a 'magic number' and is used in the Golden Rectangle. A Golden Rectangle is created by making the length 1.6 times longer than the width. Often, when we freehand draw a rectangle, it ends up being to the above proportion. Use this knowledge when designing your products.

Coursework

Freehand sketching using grids and underlays are useful techniques to help create 3D ideas – an important skill to master for assessment.

Activities

1 Use an everyday object and sketch it freehand from different viewpoints.

2 Use two different types of underlay grids and produce more accurate sketches of the same object.

3 Practise freehand sketching in isometric, using no grids or rulers.

Summary

★ Freehand sketches help develop the design of 3D objects.

★ Crating helps designers to draw objects more accurately in 3D.

★ Grids help to produce work to a more consistent quality and also save time.

2.2 Enhancement techniques: Rendering

In this chapter you will:
★ learn how to make drawings and sketches look realistic.

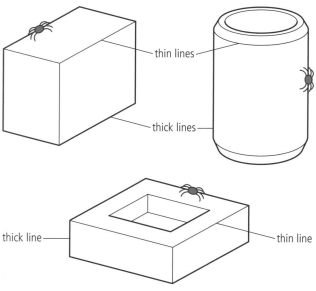

thin lines

thick lines

thick line

thin line

Adding realism

Rendering is the name given to the process of adding surface texture to an object to make it look realistic. To make drawings stand out, designers use a variety of techniques to show the form of an object. The form of an object is the 3D shape.

Thick and thin line technique

One quick and easy way of adding impact to a drawing is to apply the thick and thin line technique. A simple way of applying a thick and thin line is to imagine a spider walking over the edge of an object. If the spider disappears over the edge, it will be a thick line. If it is still visible, it will be thin line. Thick lines should be about twice as thick as thin lines.

Highlighting

Sometimes a drawing, even with thick and thin lines applied, needs to be enhanced further to make it more noticeable. This is particularly important at the initial design stages when presenting ideas for discussion.

There are two basic methods. The first is to add colour around the outside of a drawn object where any handy media can be used, for example colouring pencils, spirit markers or paint wash. The second method is to add colour to the surface of the object and to leave white areas free of colour along the edges of an object where light is being reflected.

Light and shade

To achieve a good effect, it is important to understand how light affects each surface of an object. When you produce a pictorial (3D) drawing of an object, the outline defines the shape. In reality, you never see the outline of an object, just the different areas of light and shade.

When applying light and shade, there are two simple rules:
• The closer a surface of an object is to a light source, the lighter the tone will be. The further away it is to light, the darker the tone.
• Horizontal surfaces reflect more light than vertical surfaces.

Take care not to add too much colour as this can spoil a drawing – sometimes a little colour in the right places can make all the difference.

Tonal shading

Soft pencils such as 2B and 4B are ideal for producing a range of tones. By applying different pressure to the pencil, tonal shading is produced. The B on a pencil is short for black. The higher the number, the blacker the pencil. For example, 7B is much blacker than 2B. See page 58 for more information on sketching and drawing equipment.

Tonal shading

Line shading

An alternative method of shading is to use lines. By varying the number of lines, the spaces between them and the thickness of each line, it is possible to achieve an effective finish. It is also much quicker than tonal shading.

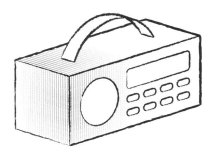

Line shading

Hatch shading

This is a similar method to line shading except that crossed lines are used to highlight shaded areas.

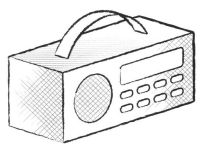

Hatch shading

Dot shading

This uses dots created with a pencil or fine-liner to highlight shaded areas. This method can be very effective, but it takes time to do well and can make a mess of your pens.

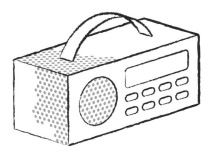

Dot shading

Shadows

Adding shadows to an object will make it appear to be resting on a surface and give it a more realistic look. Simple shadows are easy to create, but accurate shadowing needs to be worked out using technical drawing methods. A good method is to set up a light source, like an angle poise lamp, and observe the shadows created. See where they are at their most intense and how they fade the further they are from the light source.

Ic Coursework

You are expected to show a variety of different graphic techniques in your coursework to achieve the highest marks.

Activities

1 Explain why shading a drawing of an object is an important feature of graphic illustration.

2 Draw simple shapes like a cube, a cylinder and a sphere and then experiment freely with various rendering techniques to see what works best. Try to develop your own personal style.

Summary

★ Shading techniques help to add realism to drawings and sketches.

★ The difference between light and dark is called contrast and helps to define the form of an object.

★ The edges of an object reflect light and can be highlighted using a white pencil or by leaving the edge free from colour.

Design skills

2.3 Enhancement techniques: Textures

In this chapter you will:

★ **learn about how simple rendering techniques can be used to create texture on the surface of an object.**

The surface of a material can be shiny, rough, smooth, hard, non-reflective or soft. These words describe the feel or texture of a surface. We can see texture (as well as feel it) because of the way light falls onto the surface. A rough surface such as a brick is made up of many lumps and hollows. The lumps cast shadows and the hollows do not reflect as much light as raised surfaces and appear darker.

Many of the materials used in graphic products have textured surfaces. By studying the way light falls onto a surface, we can use a range of techniques to represent the shadows, patterns and reflections seen.

As a graphic designer you will need to be able to produce rendered drawings conveying different materials and surfaces, such as:

- wood
- metal
- plastic
- glass
- polished
- rough
- opaque
- transparent.

Some of the enhancement techniques already described on pages 18–19 can be used to create a textured look on a surface. Tone, dots and lines can be used to show the surface texture of an object and/or material.

For example, parallel lines can be used to suggest a shiny surface, while dots can be used to show a dimpled surface like leather. A variety of lines can be used to represent wood grain, while small circles can be used to give the impression of small pockets and holes on a rough surface like a bathroom sponge or a block of concrete. Broad stripes of dark tone can be used to give the impression of a metal tube or cylinder. Use whatever media seems suitable to create the best effect. The examples below show what can be achieved. Practice and experimentation is needed to perfect each technique.

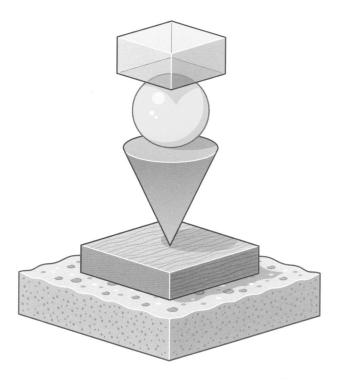

Tone, dots and lines can be used to show surface texture

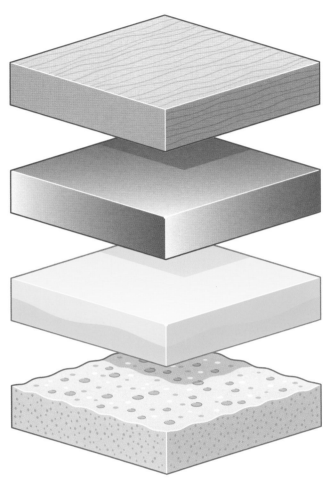

Rendered drawings convey different materials and surfaces

Placing a piece of paper over the surface and rubbing it lightly with a pencil or crayon can achieve some rendered texture patterns. The same technique can be used to copy the texture created when a material has a formed surface like a fine wire mesh.

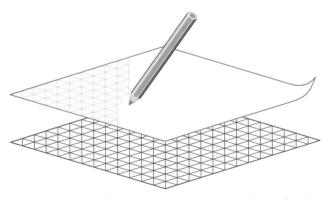

Rubbing pencil over a wire mesh gives a patterned texture

Computer rendering

Some computer rendering programmes like those in CorelDRAW and Pro/DESKTOP can create very realistic rendered images.

Computer-rendered objects

Activity

Copy the outlines of the objects in this chapter and render them to match the materials and surfaces described.

Summary

★ It is important to show texture in design drawings because it helps to make a more effective presentation.

★ Drawings produced with added texture are more visually interesting.

★ Use textural representation to convey different materials and surfaces.

Design skills

Colour theory

In this chapter you will:

★ **learn about the basic principles of colour theory**

★ **learn how the language of colour is used by designers in the manufacture of graphic products.**

Colour is an essential ingredient in the success of all graphic products and is part of the world around us. It affects the way we feel about and react to everyday things. Deciding on the most suitable colour for a design can be complicated, so careful selection is necessary.

Primary, secondary and tertiary colours

Primary (first) colours are red, yellow and blue. They are called primary because they cannot be made from other colours, and from these colours (with black and white used for tone) nearly all other colours can be made.

Secondary colours are made by mixing pairs of primary colours together. The result is orange (red and yellow), purple (blue and red) and green (yellow and blue).

Tertiary colours are made by mixing one primary and one secondary colour.

The colour wheel

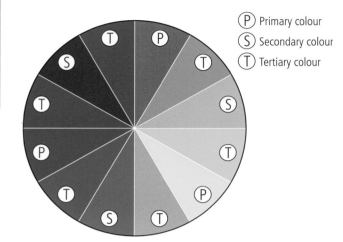

(P) Primary colour
(S) Secondary colour
(T) Tertiary colour

The colour wheel

Using colour in design

Complimentary colours

Colours that are opposite each other on the colour wheel create contrast and improve the appearance of each other. These colours are called complimentary colours.

- orange compliments blue
- red compliments green
- yellow compliments purple.

Harmonising colours

Neighbouring colours on the colour wheel, like yellow and orange, are called harmonising colours. This means they work in harmony with each another.

Because harmonising colours such as yellow and green are close together on the colour wheel, they do not create much contrast. Therefore, they should not be used on products that need to be photocopied because the colours blend together and the image loses its quality and definition.

Colours that harmonise, such as orange and red, can be blended together with a pencil to give pleasing graphic effects. This can only be achieved with neighbours on the colour wheel.

Hue and tone

Hue is the quality we identify by a colour name, such as red or purple. Tone is the amount of light and dark used to change the hue: white to lighten it and black to darken it.

Colour messages

Some colours have traditionally been associated with certain emotional responses. For example, red is often associated with danger; yellow and black stripes (like those on some insects or on the back of large vehicles) are a warning. White, although not a colour, is used in cleansing products as it gives the impression of being clean and sterile. Some colours give responses of temperature, for example cool/cold colours are those in the blue hues, while warm/hot colours are those in the red and orange hues. Cultural differences also affect colour association. Muslims, for example, see green as a holy colour, while for Greeks white is often seen as representing water.

Designing with colour

To ensure a successful colour scheme is created for a product, a good deal of experimentation is required. Use a range of harmonious hues and tones, and then add a small amount of one complimentary colour. To help, consider the following points:

- Warm colours tend to make an object appear closer to the viewer than cold colours.
- This same effect also makes a warm-coloured object appear larger than a similar-sized cold-coloured object.
- The cold-coloured object will appear to look heavier even though it may be the same size as the warm-coloured one.

Colour fusion

When small dots of colour are placed next to each other they appear to blend, creating a new colour when viewed from a distance. For example, a mixture of yellow and blue dots gives the impression of being green. This technique has been used by artists such as Monet, Seurat and Van Gogh and is called pointillism.

A colour television uses a screen made up of thousands of dots. Each dot emits either red, green or blue/violet light (RGB). When mixed at different levels, they create the impression of a real image. Note that a television uses additive colour mixtures so that when they are mixed together white light is produced.

Colour separation

Modern colour printing uses magenta, yellow and cyan inks and, together with black, form the four-colour process. If you use a magnifying glass to examine colour pictures, you will see they are made up of tiny dots printed in these three hues and black, which gives the tone. Colour separation is described in more detail on page 111.

✏ Activities

1 Examine a range of packaging materials and explain how colour has been used to communicate information about the product.

2 Experiment with a range of colouring media using different colouring techniques to test out a variety of colour schemes for one of the packages examined above.

Summary

★ Colours are known are primary, secondary or tertiary.

★ Colours influence feelings, emotions and expectations.

★ Colours can look hot, warm, cold, cool, heavy, light, near or far.

Design skills

2.5 Presenting your ideas to a client

> **In this chapter you will**
> ★ **learn how to present design concepts to a client.**

How you present your ideas to a client can make the difference between success and failure. Therefore, it is important to get your concept across in the most effective way. To do this convincingly, professionals use a variety of techniques:

- 2D and 3D pictorial drawings
- small-scale and full-scale models
- working engineering drawings
- photographs
- computer presentations
- verbal presentations
- written reports.

The nature of the product and the needs of the client, together with the type of information to be presented, will influence what techniques are used.

Considering the product

The character of the product must be taken into account. It is best to choose a style of presentation that suits the image of the product. For example, a child's play radio can be presented in a simple, colourful style, similar that used in children's books, whereas a high-tech piece of equipment like a hi-fi system would probably benefit from a more technical style.

The needs of the client

The client's needs must be considered. It could be that all a client is looking for is a simple restyling of an existing product – perhaps there is little time or a limited budget. In this instance, a series of **presentation drawings** could be used to show the changes, as these can be produced quickly and economically. However, if the client is responsible for a major new development like the design of a shopping centre, the presentation could use all the techniques mentioned above.

Choose a presentation style that suits the product

The client's needs must be considered when presenting ideas

What information should be conveyed?

The type of presentation techniques used should relate to the type of information to be conveyed. For example, the costings for a project would be best presented as a written report, perhaps with some use of **Information and Communication Technology (ICT)**. Manufacturing details are best presented by a series of **working drawings**, perhaps with **flow charts** to explain the sequence of manufacture.

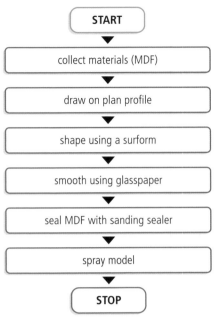

START

↓

collect materials (MDF)

↓

draw on plan profile

↓

shape using a surform

↓

smooth using glasspaper

↓

seal MDF with sanding sealer

↓

spray model

↓

STOP

The presentation techniques should reflect the information to be conveyed

Coursework

Presenting your ideas requires you to follow an industrial process – this is encouraged by AQA for coursework projects.

Activities

1 Use the following list of products to decide which methods of presentation could be used to best communicate each concept.
   a A leaflet holder (POSD).
   b A CD cover.
   c An MP3 music player.
   d A room layout for a coffee shop.

2 For each of the above products, decide what information should be conveyed.

Summary

★ A variety of techniques are used to convey concepts to a client.

★ The client's needs are an important factor in deciding how to present an idea.

Pictorial drawings

In this chapter you will:

★ learn how to produce 3D views to give your designs a more realistic appearance.

Pictorial drawings show an object in 3D. Pictorial drawing methods are used to give a realistic impression of what a product will look like and to communicate ideas to a client.

Look at the drawings below. The first is produced in 2D, while the second is drawn in 3D. It is easy to see which one shows more detail, giving a clearer idea of what it is.

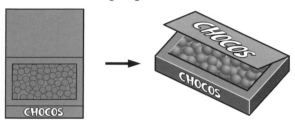

2D and 3D drawings

Sketching in 2D is the simplest method of drawing (see pages 16–17). However, at presentation stage, a higher-quality drawing is necessary. The most useful pictorial drawing methods are **perspective** drawing and **isometric** projection.

Perspective drawing

Perspective drawing is based on the principle that the closer an object is to you, the bigger it appears to be. Conversely, the further away the object is, the smaller it appears. The classic example of this is looking down a dead straight railway track. The lines of the tracks appear to converge towards a vanishing point that appears to be on the horizontal line at eye-level to the viewer.

There are various perspective drawing methods, but the most useful ones are one-point and two-point perspective.

One-point perspective

This is the simplest method to employ. It uses only one vanishing point and the object can be positioned above or below eye level. This makes it possible to see the front and top or front and bottom of the object. Remember that all the lines on the side of an object go back towards the vanishing point. One-point perspective drawing is good for showing simple views of room interiors or exhibition spaces.

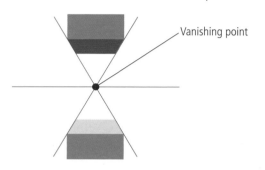
Vanishing point

One-point perspective

Two-point perspective

Two-point perspective drawing gives a realistic form of pictorial drawing. It uses two vanishing points, allowing the viewer to see three sides of an object.

Two-point perspective drawings start with the front corner of the object. This gives the effect of it being drawn at a slight angle. All lines except the vertical lines are then drawn back towards the appropriate vanishing point.

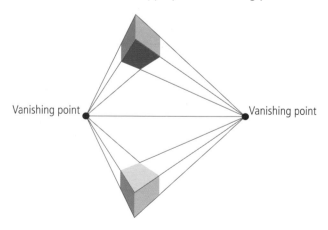
Vanishing point   Vanishing point

Two-point perspective

Drawing circles and cylinders

A circle drawn in perspective will appear as an ellipse. The best way to construct a circle is to first draw a crate. From this, find the centre by joining the diagonal lines and then find the mid points of each line. Lightly draw a curve between each point and complete the ellipse until it looks right.

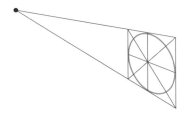

A circle drawn in one-point perspective using a crate

To create a cylinder, the same method is used at each end and then the lines joining the edges of the ellipses can be drawn to complete the cylinder.

Isometric projection

Isometric drawing is a good method of producing realistic views of an object. Formal isometric drawings follow certain guidelines, but this method is also an excellent guide for freehand sketching.

Rules

In isometric projection, the horizontal lines of an object are drawn at 30° to the horizontal. All lines are drawn to their full-scale size and the front corner of the object is drawn first. Isometric projections show three sides of an object, and because all lines are drawn to the same scale, the drawing can look a bit odd. However, it means that measurements can be taken off the page, which can be useful when communicating a design.

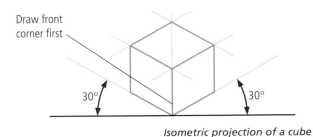

Draw front corner first

30°   30°

Isometric projection of a cube

Design skills

2.7 Working drawings 1: Orthographic projections

In this chapter you will:

★ learn how to produce working drawings using a variety of techniques and conventions that provide a manufacturer with all the details required to make a product.

Working drawings follow certain conventions and provide all the necessary information that a manufacturer might need such as dimensions, material specifications, quality requirements, finishes and, where relevant, assembly details.

Orthographic projections

An orthographic projection is the main type of working drawing used by all manufacturers worldwide. Unlike a pictorial drawing, orthographic projections view each face of an object separately in two dimensions (2D).

Conventions

In Europe, the convention used is called **third angle projection**. The arrangement of a drawing on a page and its dimensions are defined by the **British Standards Institute (BSI)**. This provides a common standard that everyone can follow.

Plans and elevations

Orthographic projections use a language of their own. A view looking down on an object is called the plan. A view from the front or end is called a front or end elevation.

Arrangements of a drawing

The arrangement of the plan, front and end elevations should match the minimum number of views needed to show all the information – usually three. In third angle drawings, a standard symbol is used to identify the convention.

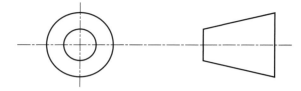

Third angle symbol

The symbol shows an end elevation and a front elevation of a cone with the top removed.

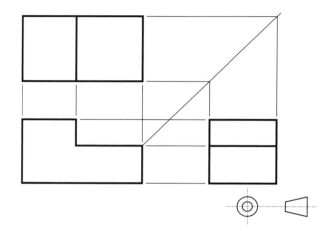

A third angle orthographic projection

Note that the above drawing includes construction lines. These are used to ensure all the views are kept in line and to help construct the drawing when using drawing instruments.

Orthographic projections in action

Orthographic projections are drawn with precision and to scale. The scale of a drawing must always be shown. It may be that a very small item needs to be magnified on the page to make it easier to understand. In this case, it could be drawn at a scale of 2:1 (twice full size). If a very large object is being drawn, it may need to be reduced in size. In this case, it could be drawn to a scale of 1:2 (half full size). However, no matter what the drawn scale is, the dimensions of each feature are written to actual size.

Line types

Orthographic projections use different styles of lines and lines with different thicknesses. The following list covers the main types needed:

- Feint lines: used for construction lines. ————————
- Long dashed lines (a long dash followed by a short dash): used for centre lines and drawn at a thickness of 0.3 mm. —— — — —— — —— — —— —
- Dimension lines: drawn at a thickness of 0.3 mm. ————
- Internal lines of an object: drawn at a thickness of 0.5 mm. ————————
- Outline of an object: drawn at a thickness of 0.7 mm. ————————
- Hidden detail lines: drawn using short dashed lines at a thickness of 0.5 mm. – – – – – – – – – – – –

Hidden detail/sectional views

It is sometimes difficult to show all the detail of an object using normal plan and elevation views. Detail that is difficult to see, or is inside an object, requires an imaginary section to be cut through so the detail can be revealed. An imaginary slice is made through the object and then a view is drawn of what is revealed. The view is drawn in a suitable place on the page and labelled as a sectional view. Where the slice has gone through a solid part of the object, it is shaded using hatching lines drawn evenly at 45° using a set square. Areas that are not cut through are left blank.

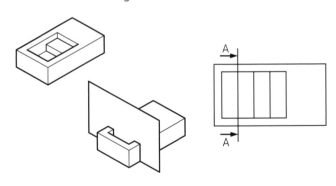

Sectional views

Assembly drawings

Many products are made up a number of parts. An assembly drawing shows a number of these parts joined together. This could be a whole assembly of a product or a sub-assembly that forms part of yet another assembly drawing.

Assembly drawings should show how the parts are joined together and any special instructions. They should also include a parts list so that all the parts can be identified.

The parts will be numbered and details of materials, quantity and sizes given. If the same component is being used in more than one place, this is identified by a number underneath the circle.

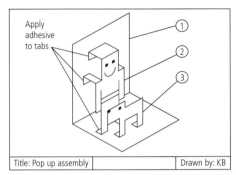

Part no.	Part title	Material/componant	Qty
Item 1	Card backing	Board	1
Item 2	Robot body	Board	1
Item 3	Robot dog	Board	1

An assembly drawing and parts list

✎ Activities

1 Produce an orthographic projection of a familiar household object. Use one with a regular shape.
   a Start by doing a quick orthographic sketch.
   b Then measure the object before completing a more accurate drawing using instruments and a drawing board.
2 Complete the same exercise by doing the final drawing using a suitable CAD program like Techsoft 2D Design or Pro/DESKTOP.

Summary

★ Orthographic projections are used as working drawings. They contain all the information required for manufacture.

★ A good way of understanding how to produce an orthographic projection is to think of a product folding out like a piece of packaging.

★ Assembly drawings show parts put together and include a parts list.

★ BS308 is the British Standard that orthographic engineering drawings work to.

Design skills

In this chapter you will:

★ **learn about architectural drawings**

★ **learn how the various types of architectural drawings are used to communicate information to builders, planners and the public.**

Architectural drawings are made to visualise the design of buildings and structures and to provide all the information for construction to take place. Local authorities use them to consider and approve building projects. The architect responsible refers to the drawings when overseeing a building project and guides the builders during construction.

Plans

These are 2D drawings that give an overhead view of the area in question. In the case of a building, a separate drawing is required for each floor. Plans are usually drawn to a scale of 1:50 as standard and will show all doorways, internal walls or partitions, windows, stairways, etc. All aspects are drawn to the exact shape and proportion. Site plans show the layout of the building in relation to its surroundings.

Elevations

An elevation is a view from the front, sides and rear of a building. These are normally drawn to a scale of 1:100 and include such detail as window heights, door positions, type of roof, wall rendering, brickwork patterns, etc. They are used in conjunction with plan views when applying to the local authority for planning applications.

Some elevation drawings may be artistically rendered to make them look more realistic, particularly when they are on display in council offices or at a sale office where the public may view them.

Sectional views

These are similar in style to sectional views in orthographic projections (see pages 28–29). An imaginary slice is taken through a building at an appropriate place and then any solid part that is 'cut' is hatched. These drawings are important and are usually drawn at a scale of 1:50, but sometimes – to show detail more clearly – they are drawn to a scale of 1:20. Sectional views show the height of all the floors and stairwells, and include details of wall and roof construction.

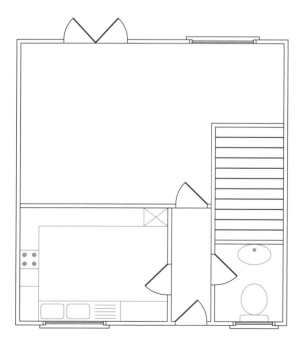

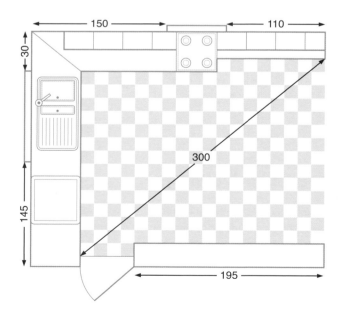

Plan views

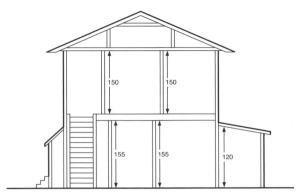

A sectional view through a building

Planometric drawings

Information from a set of architectural plans can be used to create a planometric drawing. These are fairly easy to produce and will turn a 2D plan into a 3D image. The plan is rotated through an angle of 30° or 45°, and then details from the plan are added. Vertical heights are drawn to real scale size. This type of drawing gives a better idea of what the building or structure will look like.

One advantage of planometric drawings is that circles which are parallel to the plan can be drawn easily using a compass.

Coursework

It is essential that a good, clear working drawing is included within your coursework portfolio.

Activities

1 Produce a plan view of the layout of your bedroom, using a scale of 1:50.

2 Convert the plan drawn in Activity 1 into a planometric drawing showing the height of the walls and position of furniture.

Summary

★ Architects use plan drawings to show details of each floor in a building.

★ Architects use elevation drawings to show the external sides of a building.

★ Sectional views are used to show an imaginary slice through a building.

★ Planometric drawings are used to convert a 2D plan into a 3D drawing, making it easier to visualise what the building or structure will look like.

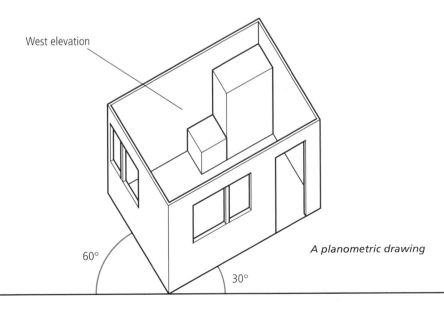

West elevation

60°

30°

A planometric drawing

Design skills

Information drawings

In this chapter you will:
★ **learn about the different types of research data a designer might use**
★ **learn the methods that can be used to present data in a form that is easy to understand.**

Research involves collecting information, and how this data is presented is important. It is often easier to understand data in the form of a graph, picture or table rather than as a collection of figures.

Types of data

There are two main types of data:
- Quantitative data: this is information that can be measured and is often produced from questionnaires where everyone is asked the same question. The results can be analysed and conclusions made.
- Qualitative data: this is data that cannot be measured. It is usually produced from observations and interviews where people's views are taken into account. This type of information tends to be used to show trends or patterns in behaviour or choice.

Methods of presenting information

Presenting information is an important part of the design process. The type of graph or chart chosen not only helps to make the information easier to understand, it also makes it more interesting. There are four main methods, all of which can be presented in 2D and 3D form:
- pie charts
- line graphs
- bar charts
- pictograms.

Pie charts

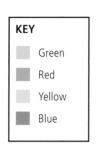
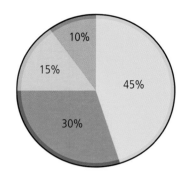

A pie chart

These are a quick and easy way of presenting quantitative data, where information you have gained can be presented as a percentage of the whole. Pie charts give instant feedback and can be enhanced by drawing them in 2D or 3D form, as well as by using colour rendering or showing a segment partly removed to emphasise a particular point.

Line graphs

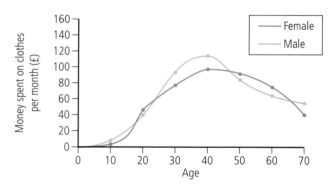

A line graph

Line graphs are one of the most common ways of displaying quantitative information. They are normally used to show the changing relationship between two factors, of which one may be time. They are simple in that they use a line to connect a series of points or crosses. The effect is easy to read and understand.

Bar charts

Bar charts are good for making comparisons between two pieces of information, perhaps from a questionnaire. They are often called histograms and enable you to make quick

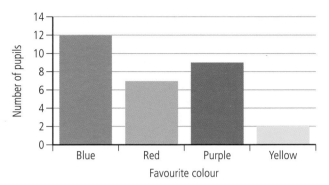

A bar chart

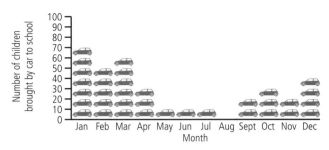

A pictograph uses pictograms to convey information

visual comparisons of the answers to questions. It is easy to see which is the biggest or smallest in any category. As with pie charts, both line graphs and bar charts can be made to look more interesting by adding colour or by making them three dimensional. Computers are good at creating charts and graphs, often with built-in facilities for displaying data in a graphical form.

Pictograms

Pictograms are graphic symbols that are used instead of words. They do not rely on people speaking the same language and can communicate information using less space. Many pictograms have become universally standard and need only a quick glance for people to know what they mean.

What do these pictograms represent?

Good places to find pictograms are in areas where lots of people visit, like cinemas, theatres, campsites and shops.

Pictographs use the idea of a pictogram in a graph or chart. In a bar chart, for example, pictograms could be used to represent the information on display. In the following example, pictograms of a motor car have been used to show car use over a year.

Using charts and graphs can not only help to make your GCSE coursework look lively and interesting, it can also demonstrate your creative ability when representing the results of your research.

Coursework

★ Always try to use visual representation of data rather than straight text as this makes it easier to understand.

★ Use appropriate types of data presentation in your analysis of research. Be creative in how the information is presented, but make sure the data is easy to understand.

Activities

1 Explain why pictograms may be more beneficial for displaying information about facilities in an international campsite.

2 Design a pictogram for displaying information about people's favourite food.

3 Explain the advantages of using a graph or chart to display information rather than a database containing a set of figures.

Summary

★ There are two main types of data: quantitative and qualitative.

★ Graphs and charts are good ways of showing numerical information in a graphical, easy-to-read way.

★ Pictograms use pictures or symbols to represent information without words.

Design skills

Signs, symbols and labels

In this chapter you will:
★ **learn about signs, symbols and labels**
★ **learn how colour and the three types of symbol – enactive, iconic and symbolic – are used in graphic products.**

Communicating information

One of the main aims of a graphic designer is to communicate information. Designers often have to communicate complex information in a clear and concise manner, often with limited space and in a way that avoids confusion. Good design means making information and instructions easy to follow.

Impact graphics

Graphic designers use a range of design imagery including signs, symbols and words to get across a message. Often called impact graphics, this form of graphics is used to persuade a consumer to buy a product, to warn about danger, to instruct or to inform.

Colour is a major component in any graphic design. When applied to attention-grabbing symbols, signs and words, colour can make the difference between success and failure. The colour red, for example, is a bold, aggressive colour. It stands out well against a white background and is good for making warning signs.

What is the difference between a sign, a symbol and a label?

A sign tends to give an instruction or a warning, such as a road sign or an exit sign above a door. A symbol is a pictorial image that represents something, often a simplified picture of an object. The symbols on a car dashboard, representing things like the engine, headlights or heater, are good examples. A label is something that is applied to an object. It could be attached physically, like a headlamp symbol on a switch, or it could be more abstract, like the use of colour to tell the difference between full-fat (blue), semi-skimmed (green) and skimmed milk (red).

Types of symbol

In the world of symbol design, there are three main categories:
• enactive (action) symbols
• iconic (pictorial) symbols
• symbolic (abstract) symbols.

Enactive (action) symbols

These symbols use imagery that shows something happening, like a sign showing a picture of a pedestrian crossing a road, or symbols on a computer keyboard indicating page up or down.

Enactive symbols on a computer keyboard

Iconic (pictorial) symbols

These symbols, often called pictograms, tend to show a stylised (simplified image) graphic of an object or activity. Many pictograms involve stylised images of people, like those seen on the doors of male and female toilets. It is important when designing pictograms that the essential features of the object are reproduced so that they are easily recognisable without being over-detailed.

Iconic symbols often use stylised graphics of people

Symbolic (abstract) symbols

These are often symbolic in nature. They use images that represent a concept, category or word association. A good example of this is the Olympic symbol, where five interlocking rings represent the five inhabited continents, with each ring a different colour on a white background.

Symbolic symbols are often abstract

The role of colour in labelling

Certain colours mean certain things when associated with symbols used in labels. The British Standards Institute produces guidelines and recommendations on all types of labels and signs. For safety signs, the colour red means to prohibit (for example, no entry signs), green represents safety (for example, 'go' on a set of traffic lights) and black and yellow mean danger, especially on dangerous machinery. Many products, like milk, are now solely recognised by the colour they are labelled with. We do not even have to read what the product is – it has become instinctive. How many other products can you think of that use colour labelling to the same effect?

Symbols in action

Symbols are used in many forms. Pictograms, for example, are good at communicating objects and images without language barriers. No words are used and the image can be recognised by everyone.

Symbols can be used on their own or in combination to direct or instruct. In this form, they are usually called signs. We have become used to reading the shorthand of signs, with road signs being the most familiar. These signs have been designed carefully so that in less than a second

we can read them, understand them and act upon them without really thinking. In many ways, signs are a language all of their own and, just like the written word, need to be learned before we can use them efficiently.

Another use for symbols is in communicating instructions. Processes can be broken down into easily understood stages using a variety of symbols, words and sequences. Look at the instructions on the side of a packet of washing powder or on a bottle of stain remover. Try to work out what each stage in the process is.

Activities

1. Collect a range of symbols and sort them into enactive, iconic and symbolic symbols.

2. Design a set of symbols or pictograms for use in school to label rooms based on which subject is taught there.

3. Use sketches and notes to explain your understanding of the term 'stylisation'.

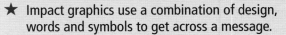

Summary

★ Impact graphics use a combination of design, words and symbols to get across a message.

★ Symbols must be easy to understand in any language.

★ Symbols can be categorised into three main types: enactive, iconic and symbolic.

★ The use of colour is important in symbols.

Design skills

In this chapter you will:

★ **learn about the different categories of typographic styles**

★ **how size and layout of text on a page are used to communicate information and create impact.**

Typography is the art and layout of type on a page, with the word 'type' meaning a letter or character. The appearance of type on a page can be used to attract attention, add impact, give a decorative look or give an impression of a particular time and place.

Typefaces

Graphic designers need to select **typefaces** carefully. They need to specify the style of type (font), its size and weight, its colour and the space around it.

Most graphic designers use existing typefaces. It is possible to buy font packages with thousands of different styles of text. However, you may want to create your own. One approach is to alter an existing font or to simply change one letter in a word to create impact.

Each style of lettering has its own particular identity. Different typefaces can express a wide variety of feelings. The ability to choose the correct style of text for a graphic design is important. Collect a variety of magazines, newspapers, books and posters and look at the typefaces used in relation to the information being presented.

Giddyup giggles with *Happiness*

Folio Extra Bold makes the reader feel **Sad**

Avenir Heavy should be take **Seriously**

Arriba Arriba is **Fun!**

Times Roman conveys Authority

Garamond Handtooled can make it **Traditional**

Broadway Engraved expresses **Nostalgia**

Different typefaces convey different messages

Size

Type is measured in points. One point is equal to 1/72nd of an inch (about 0.25 mm). A letter with a size of 72 points would be about 25 mm high. The width of a letter is also important. Most typefaces come in a range of widths. You can see these by scrolling through the fonts on a **desktop publishing (DTP)** programme.

Generally, the more condensed or lighter a letter is, the larger it needs to be to be read easily. Conversely, the bolder a letter type is, the smaller it can be.

For example:
• lighter text needs to be bigger
• **bolder text can be smaller**.

Most books use a type of size 10 or 12 points for the main text, while headings may be as big as 16 points. Magazines tend to use smaller type, although many headings or attention-grabbing words can be much bigger.

Categories of type

For general use, there are four basic categories of type:
• Serif: these typefaces have a 'tail' at the end of each stroke. Serif type is used for main body text. It is easy to read and looks traditional.
• Sans serif: these typefaces have no 'tails'. Sans serif type is bold and strong, and plain and clear to read. It is mostly used for titles and headings.
• Script: these typefaces tend to look handwritten and have a more personal feel. Not easy to read, but can be effective.
• Stylised or decorative: these typefacesare designed to attract attention and give text some meaning or association.

Serif

Sansserif

Script

Decorative

The four basic type categories

Spacing

The spaces between letters, words and lines are important. In this book, standard spacing has been used. However, by altering the amount of space between each element, it is possible to get more text on a page or to fill up more space and make text easier to read.

The standard space between each word is half that of the lower case 'o'. Any bigger and weird patterns called rivers can occur on the page, making the text difficult to read.

Justification

Justification means how text is aligned. The position of words on a page can be:
- centre justified
- left justified
- right justified
- fully justified.

Most text is printed in columns using one of these methods. For example:

Centre justified is where each line of text is centralised to the middle of the page, column or text box.

Left justified is where each line is aligned to the left margin or page.

Right justified is where each line is aligned to right side of the page or margin. It is often used to align captions next to pictures or images.

Fully justified is where each line is aligned with both sides of the page or column, left and right. This formatting is commonly used in columns in newspapers and magazines. However, because words vary in length, the spaces between them need to be adjusted. Adjusting the spacing is called kerning. This can be done automatically using a word processor or DTP programme.

Design skills

Surface developments: Nets 1

In this chapter you will:

★ **learn how a simple 3D container can be developed from a flat sheet and the standard conventions for lines used on nets.**

A net, or surface development, is the flat shape of a carton or display stand that has been unfolded. Nets vary from the basic rectangular form of a simple cosmetics box through to highly complex cartons such as wine bottle carriers used in supermarkets.

Nets are the unfolded shapes of cartons and display stands

Virtually all nets are based on basic geometric shapes such as circles, squares and triangles. A good example of a surface development based on a simple geometric shape is the Toblerone chocolate bar.

Cut and fold lines

When nets are drawn, they contain a range of different line types. Each line type has a particular meaning. It is important that these lines are used consistently, otherwise the manufacturers may make mistakes and end up cutting along a line that needed to be folded. The five main line types are:

Cut

– · – · – · – · – · – · – · –

Crease

· ·

Perforate

– – – – – – – – – – – – – – –

Score and crease

——— · – · — · – · — · – · ———

Cut and crease

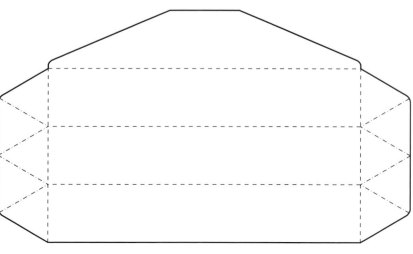

The Toblerone bar is a good example of a carton developed from a simple geometric shape

Joining

Nets are joined together using tabs. Nets must always have tabs so that they can fit together. The tabs overlap the edges where the sides meet and are often glued in place. This is a common way of joining food packaging. Most cartons use a combination of glue and self-locking closure methods. This is done to reduce the cost of packaging and to increase the speed of production.

Windows

Often designers want to cut a window or opening into the package, so the customer can see the product inside. Underwear cartons often have windows cut into them, but care should be taken as these can significantly reduce the strength of the packaging.

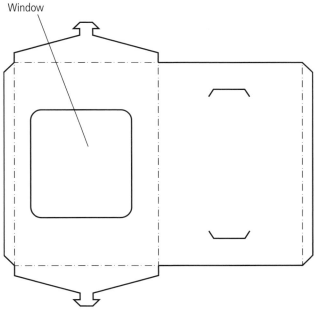

Window

A net of packaging for ladies' tights – the window allows the customer to see the product

Folding a net

When folding a net (developing its form), the fold lines are creased. The main body of the carton is formed first, then the edges are glued or slotted into place.

Activities

1 For each shape below, sketch the net needed for their construction. Show all cut and fold lines.

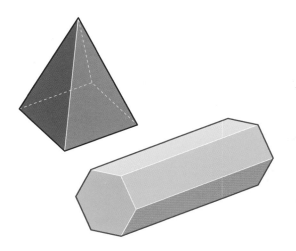

2 Collect some examples of used packaging. Carefully take them apart and sketch their nets. Pay particular attention to how they are joined.

Summary

★ A net (surface development) is the flat shape of a carton or display stand that has been unfolded.

★ It is important when designing nets that the correct line types are used.

Surface developments: Nets 2

In this chapter you will:
★ **learn about the range of different carton closures available**
★ **learn how to provide tamper-proof security to cartons.**

Carton closures

The way a carton closes or locks together is known as its closure. The type of closure used is important because it often provides or completes the carton's rigidity while also providing additional protection to the product it contains.

There are a wide variety of different closure techniques used for cartons. Each closure type has a specific function or purpose and has been chosen carefully by the designer. The most common styles for carton closures are:

• tuck-end cartons: the lids of the boxes merely tuck into place and require no gluing. Tuck-end cartons can be opened and closed many times. However, because they are not tamper-proof, they provide little security to the product

• sealed-end cartons: the flaps on the lids of these cartons are completely sealed using glue or double-sided tape

• crash-base cartons: sometimes called automatic cartons, these lock into place when folded out.

Making cartons tamper-proof

The standard tuck-end carton provides no tamper-proofing, so anyone who enters a shop or store could open the carton, tamper with the goods, then close it again and no one would know. To give customers peace of mind, manufacturers use a range of different closure adaptations designed to ensure a level of tamper-proofing to the carton.

There are four basic techniques used on tuck-end cartons, each providing a different level of tamper-proofing and complexity. These are:

• standard tuck-end carton
• slit-lock closure
• tab-lock closure
• postal-lock closure.

Tuck-end cartons

The standard tuck-end carton provides no tamper-proofing, so it is mainly used for products such as soap and other cosmetics where there is some form of secondary packaging within the carton.

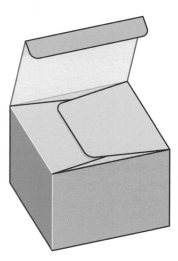

A tuck-end carton

Slit-lock closures

The slit-lock closure is very common and involves making a small cut at both sides of the tuck-in flap. Many manufacturers favour this because it is a simple and quick technique. When the carton is opened, the slits tear and provide evidence that the carton has been opened or tampered with.

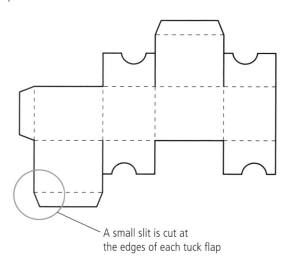

A small slit is cut at the edges of each tuck flap

A net of a slit-lock closure

Tab-lock closures

The tab-lock closure is used where a more secure seal is required. This type of closure is commonly found on perfume cartons. For additional security, a clear plastic disc is often placed over the tab.

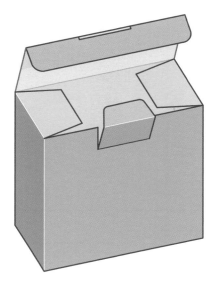

A tab-lock closure

Postal-lock closures

The postal-lock closure provides the highest level of security. The tab ends crease when the carton is opened, providing clear evidence of tampering.

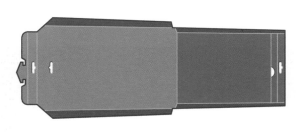

Coursework

The most important thing to remember when you design a net as part of your coursework is to consider the type of closure required. As part of the design development stage, you should consider what level of protection you need. Write your comments against your ideas and do not assume a tuck-end flap is good enough.

Activity

Collect as many different examples of cartons as possible. Look carefully at the closures that have been used. Think about the product contained in each carton and why that particular closure has been used.

Summary

★ The standard tuck-end carton provides no tamper-proofing, so carton designers have developed a range of closures to provide added protection.

★ There are four basic techniques used on tuck-end cartons: standard tuck-end, slit-lock closure, tab-lock closure and postal-lock closure.

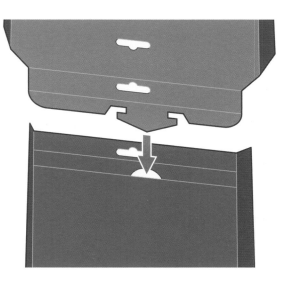

A postal-lock closure

Design skills

Surface developments: Nets 3

In this chapter you will:
★ learn what a sealed-end carton is and why it is used
★ learn how a crash-base carton closure works.

Sealed-end cartons

Sealed-end cartons, or skillets, are widely used for transit cartons. They are used by supermarkets for delivering food products such as lettuces.

Sealed-end cartons are used because they make economical use of board. This makes them a relatively low-cost carton. Look carefully at the net below and you will see that there is virtually no waste. Scrap removal is a labour-intensive and costly process.

A supermarket wine carrier

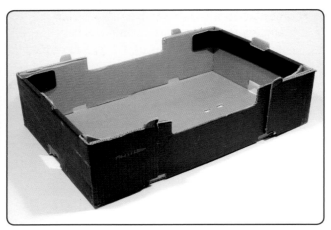

A sealed-end carton, or skillet

The flaps are completely sealed using glue or double-sided tape, which is applied on the production line using an automatic sealer.

Crash-base cartons

Automatic, or crash-base, cartons are now widely used when fast assembly is required. The crash base is applied in combination with a variety of tuck-in tops. A familiar example of a crash base carton is a supermarket wine carrier. The crash-base carton is pre-glued by the manufacturer and delivered to the supermarket in a flat form.

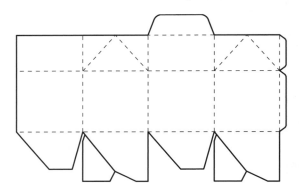

A net of a tuck-end carton with a crash base

Assembling a crash-base carton

1 The first stage is to apply glue or double-sided tape to the lengthways flap.

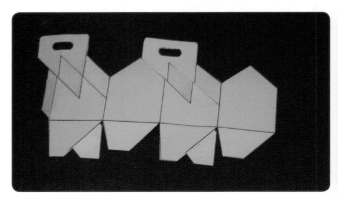

2 The next stage is to apply glue or double-sided tape to the widthways flaps and fold them into the flat-fold delivery position.

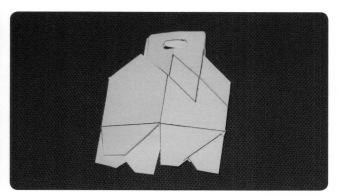

3 After applying glue or tape to the widthways flaps, the net is now folded over.

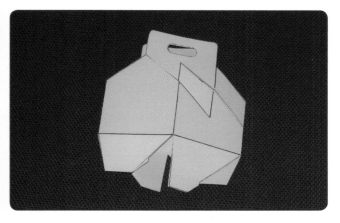

4 The crash base carton is finally assembled at the point of use. The base slides into position when the carton is pushed together. It then snaps closed using the friction between the sides of the paper/board to hold it rigid.

Activity

Visit a local supermarket and collect a wine bottle carrier that incorporates a crash base. Disassemble it carefully, then measure it and sketch the net, paying particular attention to the folds and glue tabs.

Summary

★ Sealed-end cartons, or skillets, are widely used because:
  • they are low-cost, used by supermarkets for delivering food products such as lettuces
  • they make economical use of board as there is virtually no waste.

★ Crash-base cartons are widely used because:
  • they are quick and easy to assemble
  • they can be posted in flat-pack form
  • they can be stored flat and re-used many times.

Design skills

Corporate identity

> **In this chapter you will:**
> ★ **learn how companies use graphic devices such as logos to create a particular image.**

The *Oxford English Dictionary* describes identity as 'the state of having unique identifying characteristics held by no other person or thing – the individual characteristics by which a person or thing is recognised'.

As individuals, we are easy to recognise because, generally speaking, we look different from each other. People remember us because of the way we look, speak and behave. Having an identity is just as important for businesses as it is for people.

Creating an identity

Most organisations use visual symbols or logos to separate them from other companies and to allow the public to recognise them. The best symbols are simple yet distinctive – they often say something about the organisation and give an impression of the quality of the goods or services it offers.

The Q8 oil company is a good example of how companies create visual identities. The company is owned by Kuwait Petroleum, hence the clever use of simplified initials to indicate their origin. The symbol used is simple with bold, primary colours and is easy to recognise.

The Q8 company identity

The basis of identity

Most graphic identities are based around the use of logos. Logos are part of a graphic language that we have come to understand and accept.

The word 'logo' tends to be used to represent any combination of symbols and type (words), but in fact there are distinct and different elements in a logo:

- Logogram: this is a design that uses just the initial letters of a company.
- Logotype: the most common form of logo, this uses a specially designed typeface to create a distinctive image for an organisation.
- Symbol: this is usually a stylised (simplified) image related to the organisation that helps to communicate the product or service.
- Images: these are often used as backgrounds to logograms to communicate to customers the nature of the organisation.

Combining the elements

To see how the different elements of a logo are used, take a look at the graphic identity of Typhoo tea.

The Typhoo logogram

The company use their logogram on all its products. However, this alone does not give a clear visual connection to the product, which is tea. To improve this, Typhoo combines the logogram with images of tea leaves, which make a clear visual link with the nature of the product. Product packaging shows how the combination of elements work.

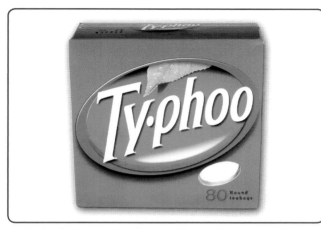

The Typhoo tea packaging combines a logogram with images of tea leaves

Use of colour

Logos often need to be photocopied and used in black and white as well as colour. Therefore, it is important that they are designed with contrasting colours. Contrasting colours make them bold and stand out. One successful combination is red and yellow. Red is an aggressive colour, which stands out, and yellow is a submissive colour, which drops into the distance.

The McDonald's logogram uses red and yellow

Trademarks

Trademarks are distinctive symbols that can contain a graphic image, company name or slogan. Some companies use just the name on their product (in the form of a logo) as their trademark – Cadbury, Nestlé and Virgin are good examples. However, while the Virgin logo is used as a basis for advertising, the different parts of the Virgin Group of companies (from Virgin Atlantic to Virgin Mobile) use it in their own unique way.

Trademarks such as Virgin are instantly recognisable

[Ic] Coursework

Most graphic products have a strong visual identity, so think carefully about this aspect when designing your coursework project.

Activities

1 List three features of a successful logo.

2 What is the difference between a logo and a trademark?

Summary

★ Most organisations use visual symbols or logos to separate them from other companies.
★ The best corporate identities are simple but distinctive.

Design skills

Creating a corporate identity

In this chapter you will:

★ learn about the different types of corporate identity and how they are used.

One of the aims of the corporate identity business is to try and help people, first of all to discover whether there is a genuine difference between their business and somebody else's; second, to express that difference if it exists; and third to help them create such a difference, where no fundamental difference exists.

Wally Olins, managing director of the Wolf Olins Corporation

What is a corporate identity?

The term 'corporate identity' refers to the visual images used by an organisation to create a particular image to project to their customers.

Corporate identity is far more than just a logo. It is the way people look, the way they behave, their uniform and the image of all the products and services the organisation provides. All of these factors project a particular image that has been designed carefully.

Corporate identity is particularly important for an organisation such as a bank or building society, because essentially all banks provide an identical service. Therefore, it is the corporate identity that highlights the uniqueness of each organisation.

Types of corporate identity

There are three different approaches to corporate identity, each of which has its advantages:

* **monolithic identity**
* **endorsed identity**
* **branded identity.**

Monolithic identity

The word 'mono' means 'one' or 'on its own'. In corporate identity terms, a monolithic identity is a single, all-encompassing style that gives a consistent graphic image to all products and services provided by the company. With a monolithic identity, the same colours are used and the same logo is applied consistently. This is a popular approach with many companies as it ties all their products together. A classic monolithic corporate identity is the Shell oil company. Just think about the colours and the logo, instantly recognisable from York to New York.

Corporate identity is a business strategy designed to produce a consistent and recognisable image

Endorsed identity

An endorsed identity is often practised by organisations such as sporting associations. It involves linking products together with an endorsement, such as a company badge, trademark or symbol. A good example of how endorsed identity works is to think about a car company such as Volkswagen. Although each model is different, and designed for a different target market with differing needs, every car incorporates a number of visual clues that link it strongly with the parent company. Companies that apply endorsed identity design are proud to be associated with the products, while at the same time recognising that each product is different.

Volkswagen uses an endorsed corporate identity

Branded identity

Many manufacturers who produce lots of different products adopt a branded identity. Although belonging to the parent company, brands have their own identity too. Branded identity allows a company to capitalise on a market and helps to eliminate competitors. Branded identity is important because many popular brands have what is known as brand loyalty among consumers. To change a brand by linking it to the parent company may risk losing this loyalty.

Branded identity means that companies such as Proctor & Gamble, owners of the Ariel brand, can capitalise on brand loyalty

Activities

1 Why do some companies adopt a corporate identity?

2 Give three examples of companies who adopt a monolithic corporate identity.

Summary

★ The term 'corporate identity' relates to the visual images used throughout an organisation to create a particular image.

★ There are three different approaches to corporate identity design: monolithic, endorsed and branded identity.

Design skills

Case study: IKEA

In this chapter you will:

★ learn how IKEA has developed a corporate identity that communicates the company's beliefs and principles to its customers.

It is not difficult to manufacture expensive fine furniture. Just spend the money and let the customers pay. To manufacture beautiful, desirable furniture at low prices is not so easy. It requires a different approach: finding simple solutions, scrimping and saving in every direction.

Ingvar Kampard, founder of IKEA

Like most successful entrepreneurs, Ingvar Kampard, the founder of the IKEA home furnishing retailer, had a clear vision and a good understanding of what customers want. By studying the philosophy behind IKEA, designers can learn an enormous amount about how to develop successful products.

Kampard believes in taking risks. Like so many successful people, he recognises that risk-taking means that sometimes you are going to make mistakes – this is part of the learning process. Kampard is reported to have said, 'Only while sleeping one makes no mistakes.'

He established IKEA in 1943 as a mail-order business. Fifteen years later he opened his first store in Sweden, selling flat-packed furniture. IKEA is now an international retailing business operating in over 30 countries with more than 70,000 employees. Sales have grown steadily every year and are now estimated to be in excess of 10 billion euros.

Creating the brand

Kampard's idea was simple: good-quality furniture, well designed, beautifully made at a cost that will suit most people. He famously said that 'people have very thin wallets. We should take care of their interests.' Furthermore, unlike his rival furniture retailers at the time, he decided that there was no point in a company spending money assembling the furniture it intends to sell when customers can do it for themselves.

IKEA furniture comes flat packed, ready for self-assembly

The IKEA logo

The name IKEA comes from the founder's initials Ingvar Kampar; the first letter of Elmtaryd, his family farm; and Agunnaryd, the village in Smaland in southern Sweden where Kampard was born.

Like most successful brands, the IKEA logo follows the easy-to-remember acronym SECRET. It is:

Simple
Easy to remember
Contrasting colours
Related to the company
Enlargeable and reducible
Transferable onto a range of different products.

The logo identifies with Sweden because it uses the colours of the Swedish national flag.

The Swedish flag

The boldness of the lettering and the contrasting colours (blue and yellow are primary colours) make the logo really stand out. The logo has a modern feel and the use of geometric shapes in its construction alludes to the clean lines within the furniture. Like most really effective logos, its colours can be interchanged without losing its dominant visual appeal.

Like many successful logos, the blue and yellow of IKEA can be interchanged without losing visual impact

A corporate identity

IKEA has always been distinctive in its approach to retailing. For example, it does not have 'customers', it has 'visitors', and it sets out to offer a 'shopping experience' rather than a quick sale. Its stores are built on large sites outside city centres and include restaurants and children's play areas. The restaurants serve Swedish food such as meatballs. The products sold have Swedish names like Ektorp, Dalarna and Aivak, and the corporate colours of the Swedish blue and yellow are used everywhere.

Coursework

As part of your research for your project, look carefully at companies like IKEA. Consider how their graphic identity contributes to the success of their brand.

Activity

Visit the IKEA website. To access the IKEA site, please go to www.heinemann.co.uk/hotlinks, insert the express code 3457P and click on the website name.

a   Make a list of the ways that the IKEA brand identity is communicated to customers.

b   Choose three different products from IKEA's online catalogue that best represent its philosophy of providing modern products that are functional yet attractive, human-centred and child friendly. For each product, explain the reasons for your choice.

Summary

★ Successful entrepreneurs take risks in the belief that making mistakes is part of the learning process.
★ IKEA has a corporate identity that relates strongly to Sweden.

Design skills

Exam questions

A container for a bottle of perfume called Alpine Essence is shown below. It has a recess for the bottle to sit in, which is formed from a net development using carton board. A carton board sleeve slides over the container. The sleeve contains all the product-related graphics and consumer information.

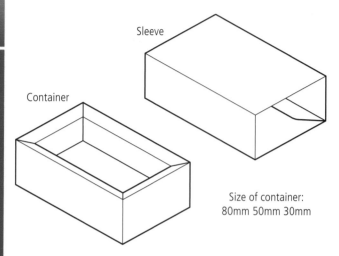

Sleeve

Container

Size of container:
80mm 50mm 30mm

1 Produce a 3D freehand sketch of the container using isometric grid paper as an underlay. *(3 marks)*

2 Produce a 3D freehand sketch of the container, with the sleeve positioned halfway down, using one-point perspective. *(3 marks)*

3 Produce a full-size net development for the container, showing all folds and tabs. *(5 marks)*

4 Produce a range of ideas for the graphics to go on the sleeve. Include appropriate images and colours related to the product name and an appropriate style of lettering. *(10 marks)*

5 Develop a final design using the ideas created in question 4 and draw this onto a net development for the sleeve. *(6 marks)*

6 Produce a working drawing using orthographic projection of the container without the sleeve fitted. Make sure all the correct symbols and conventions are used. *(6 marks)*

7 Using sketches and notes, suggest how the sleeve could be altered to allow the customer to see the product when the sleeve is fitted. *(6 marks)*

3 Materials and components

This section covers the key areas of materials and components. Focusing on how materials such as paper and board are used in the design and making of graphic products, this section provides you with information you need to select the most appropriate tools and materials to make quality products.

What's in this section?

Materials and components

Paper and board

In this chapter you will:

★ **learn about the properties of different papers and boards**

★ **learn about ways of treating paper to improve its qualities.**

What would a world without paper be like?

No newspaper to read at breakfast; no school books; no bank notes to pay for a ticket to the cinema; no letters; no faxes; no stamps to send letters (which we wouldn't have anyway); no photos of loved ones; no paper bags to carry shopping….

What is paper?

In simple terms, paper is a web-like material made of vegetable fibres or cellulose. The cellulose is extracted from both coniferous and deciduous trees and this is the main source of modern paper and board. Paper comes in a variety of weights, colours and textures. It is usually defined in terms of its weight (density) and its thickness.

Paper surface magnified 600 times

Making paper

Cellulose fibres naturally link together under certain conditions. The most common way of making paper is to mix the cellulose with water, adding a small amount of starch. This is called the pulp. When the fibres touch, they lock together forming a fragile web.

The watery pulp solution is then poured over a fine metal sieve allowing the water to drain away. The more the water drains away, the stronger the bond, although 6% water is required to retain the chemical bond. In commercial paper production, this sieve is a long, slow-moving conveyor belt. The pulp gradually forms paper as it dries. The direction that the conveyor belt is moving gives the paper its grain. It then passes through a series of polished metal rollers that press it to its desired thickness and help to give it a good surface finish. This process is known as **calendering** and it is similar to ironing the creases from a shirt.

Paper and board density

Paper density is measured in grams per square metre (gsm). This means the weight in grams of one square metre of the paper. For example, the density of normal photocopy paper is usually 80–90 gsm. Do not confuse density with thickness when describing paper. Paper thickness is measured in microns (1/1000th of a millimetre). Photocopy paper is usually between 120 and 150 microns thick. Paper is usually considered to become board when its density is more than 200 gsm. Board is often laminated (glued together) to increase its thickness.

Paper size

The most common range of papers is the A range. Each time the paper is halved in size, its value goes up by one. So A4 is half the size of A3 and A3 is half the size of A2, and so on.

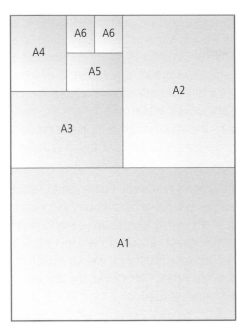

The most common range of paper size is the A range

Paper coatings

Ordinary untreated paper is of limited use to designers and manufacturers because it is absorbent, with a rough surface and an off-white colour. The most common commercial untreated paper is newsprint (the paper used for newspapers). It is so absorbent that the ink bleeds, meaning it is a poor surface for printing on to.

Newsprint is absorbent, has a poor print surface and is an off-white colour

In order to improve the surface quality of paper, coatings and fillers such as china clay and talcum are used during production. A coating is a layer of minerals that is applied to one or both sides of paper or board to improve qualities such as brightness, gloss and printability. **Uncoated** papers have a rough, more natural feel to them. Examples of uncoated papers are newsprint, cheaper catalogues and many recycled papers. These tend to be more porous and soak up ink. Uncoated stocks are ideal for quick and less precise printing. They tend to be less expensive than **coated** papers and are perfect for newspapers and flyers.

Coated papers, by contrast, have a smoother finish and are not very porous. Generally, the ink sits on this type of paper's surface, but it takes longer for the ink to dry. Type and photographs look sharper on coated stocks because the ink does not bleed into the paper.

Coatings are also used to fill up the microscopic holes in the paper's surface, making it smooth and opaque, which stops it being transparent.

Coursework

Whatever you design for your coursework project, paper will be involved. Make sure you research paper carefully and select the most appropriate type, stating its grade, thickness and desired finish.

Activity

Collect a variety of different types of paper and carry out an ink test on them using fountain pen ink. Find out which sample is the most absorbent and which one gives the best print surface.

Summary

★ Paper density is measured in grams per square metre (gsm) and paper thickness is measured in microns (1/1000th of a millimetre).

★ Paper is often coated with minerals such as china clay to improve its surface qualities.

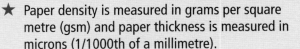

Materials and components

Different paper, different uses

In this chapter you will:

★ **learn about the issues surrounding recycling paper**

★ **learn how paper is used for different purposes in different products.**

Recycling

Over 30% of household and commercial waste is paper and cardboard. Much of it ends up in landfill sites, generating methane as it decomposes. However, it is possible to recycle clean paper and board.

The average office worker generates about 35 kg of paper waste per year. By recycling paper and buying recycled paper, we can help to slow the world's consumption of forests. Currently, 445,500 hectares of forest are cleared every day, causing:

- loss of habitats and the species that depend on them
- acceleration of global warming – trees use carbon dioxide, the main greenhouse gas
- a reduction in soil fertility.

Recycling paper is worthwhile, but is not an end in itself – waste minimisation is far more important.

Every year, more than 11 million tonnes of paper and board are used in the UK. Much of the wood pulp for this comes from Scandinavia. In order to satisfy our increasing demand for wood and paper products, the majority of the natural forests in Scandinavia have been converted into intensively managed plantations. While these forests are managed sustainably – the trees cut down for paper production are replaced – the insects and wildlife found in natural forests are not supported.

Despite the environmental and human cost of paper production, we continue to throw away vast quantities of this resource after using it only once, even though we could recycle much of it. Less than half the paper used in the UK is recovered and over five million tonnes gets dumped in landfill sites. Yet, if paper is recycled, the amount of waste is cut and less timber is used.

One of the main reasons why there is a reluctance to recycle paper is that waste paper and board often has a value of less than its handling and transport costs. Prices fluctuate considerably over time and many paper merchants charge to take it away.

Shredded carton packaging can be used instead of polystyrene chips

Some companies chip or shred their cardboard to use as packaging instead of polystyrene chips, although high levels of dust may make it unsuitable for packing high-quality products. Other options are reuse, composting and incineration, where there is a suitable combustion plant.

Local paper recycling collection networks are well-established, and many are managed by voluntary bodies. British newspapers, for example, now contain about 50% recycled content.

Common paper and boards

Material	Advantages	Uses
Newsprint	Lightweight; accepts all types of ink but better print quality is achieved with quick-drying inks; a low-cost paper	Newspapers, some leaflets and flyers
Cartridge paper	Good quality; provides a good surface for pencil, pen and markers; the name comes from its original use as the tube for a shotgun cartridge	Design drawings, sketch pads
Sugar paper	Low cost, lightweight, uncoated paper; has contrasting colours that are useful for tonal drawings	Mounting work on displays
Cardboard	Low cost, rigid paper; provides a good surface for all types of printing; generally strong and durable	Packaging, cartons and boxes
Corrugated card	Very strong yet lightweight	Packaging, particularly useful for the protection of fragile products
Bleed-proof paper	Provides an excellent surface for printing inks	High-quality writing papers
Duplex board	Cheaper than solid white board; can provide an alternative textured surface for printing	Food packaging
Cast-coated board	Similar to bleach-white card, although cast-coated board achieves a heavier and smoother finish; provides an excellent surface finish for finishing processes such as varnishing and embossing	Quality products that require a high-gloss finish
Foiled-lined lamination	Used on the surface of a variety of boards in order to achieve a waterproof layer; can be gloss or matt	Drinks or cosmetics cartons

Activities

1 Use the Internet to carry out some research into paper and board recycling in your area.

2 Produce a poster to encourage people to recycle paper and board. Include a list of reasons to explain why everyone can help.

Summary

★ Each year more than 11 million tonnes of paper and board are used in the UK. If paper is recycled, the amount of waste going to landfill is cut and less timber is used.

★ Currently 445,500 hectares of forest are being cleared every day.

Materials and components

New and smart materials

What are smart materials?

Smart materials respond in some way to an external stimulus and return to their original condition once the stimulus has been removed. For example, thermochromic (heat sensitive) pigments added to inks change colour when they are heated. When the heat is removed, they return to their original colour. Smart materials are also called intelligent or responsive materials.

Self-healing products

Many of the smart materials used in a wide range of products have been developed by the engineering and aeronautical industry. An example of this is self-healing plastic. One of the problems with plastic products is that with constant use they can start to crack. Self-healing plastics respond to cracks or breakages by repairing themselves automatically. This is done using epoxy resin adhesive (Araldite). This comes in two parts, a resin and a hardener. When these two parts are mixed together they react and 'go off', forming the adhesive. As long as the resin and hardener are kept apart, they do not work. Self-healing plastics have molecules of resin and hardener embedded within them. When a crack forms, the molecules break open and mix together, the adhesive is formed and the plastic repairs itself. This simple solution is now being used on car bumpers and aeroplanes, not only to make products last longer but also to make them safer.

Thermoplastics

Many people think thermoplastics are smart because they have a memory and can return to their original shape when reheated. However, they are not smart because, unlike all the other materials described in this chapter, they do not return to their original shape as soon as the stimulus is removed. Thermoplastics must be reheated, making them only semi-smart.

Smart inks

The main smart materials used with graphic products are pigments that can be added to printing inks to provide special or interesting effects. Common examples include thermochromic (heat sensitive), photochromic (light sensitive) and phosphorescent (glow in the dark pigments).

Inks that change colour tend to be used in graphic products to attract attention. Have you ever seen greetings cards or adverts in magazines that ask you to place your finger over a spot to reveal the answer? This works because at room temperature the ink is clear. The heat in your finger warms the ink and the answer is revealed. Products such as wine can have labels that 'reveal' graphic images at certain temperatures.

The star on the back of this beer bottle turns blue at 12°C

Photochromic inks change colour according to the level of light that falls on them.

Phosphorescent inks are commonly used in graphic products. These have the special property of being able to absorb light throughout the day, which enables them to glow in the dark.

Fire exit signs use photophorescent pigments

Products such as watches also use phosphorescent inks to make them glow in the dark

Smart oils and gels

Other smart materials in common use are those whose thickness (viscosity) can be changed. For example, high-performance racing cars need to have their engine oil at a constant thickness for maximum performance. Oil gets thinner as it warms up. In order to keep oil at a constant viscosity, racing cars use smart oils that react to electricity. As an electric current is passed through it, the oil's viscosity changes – it can therefore be controlled.

Smart gel or motion-control gel is used as an alternative to springs in a number of products such as CD players and calculators. When the CD player's door is opened, it slides out in a controlled way. This is because the gel releases its energy in a constant, controlled way.

CD Players often use smart gels to enable the draw to open in a controlled way

Smart wire

Smart wire, or shape-memory alloy (SMA), reacts to heat. When heated, it shrinks a little. It can therefore be used in graphic products such as pop-up linkages. The heat comes in the form of a small electric current that is passed through the wire. When the button is pushed, the wire shrinks, tugging on the pop-up.

Conductive plastics

Another interesting smart graphic product is conductive plastic film. This thin plastic can be used to measure pressure – the higher the pressure applied to it, the more current it gives off. So if a small sheet of this film is placed inside someone's shoe, it is possible to analyse the way they walk.

Piezo electric crystals (quartz)

Piezo crystals pulse regularly when electricity is passed through them, making them perfect for watches and clocks. They are used for silent alarms – instead of an audible warning, they merely pulse (vibrate).

Coursework

Include research on new and smart materials as part of your coursework project because they add great interest to graphic products.

Activity

Use the Design inSite and eSmart websites to research five different applications of smart materials.

a To access the Design inSite site, please go to www.heinemann.co.uk/hotlinks, insert the express code 3457P and click on the website name.

b To access the eSmart site, please go to www.heinemann.co.uk/hotlinks, insert the express code 3457P and click on the website name.

Summary

★ A smart material is one that responds to an external stimulus and returns to its original condition once the stimulus has been removed.

Materials and components

Tools and equipment 1

> **In this chapter you will**
> ★ **learn which sketching and drawing tools are available and how they can be used.**

The function of any designer is to create a **prototype** of a product that satisfies a given specification and then to communicate this concept to a potential client, manufacturer or purchaser. In order to do this, a range of skills in the use of tools and equipment is required.

There are two main design situations that use tools and equipment:
- sketching and drawing
- cutting and shaping (see page 61).

Sketching and drawing

Pencils

Despite the range of new technology available, a pencil is the most important tool for a designer. The ability to draw using a pencil for sketching through to accurate technical drawings is very important. There is a range of different pencils for different tasks.

Pencils use a core of graphite material that comes in a variety of hardnesses. The type of pencil is indicated by a letter and number. Letters H, B and sometimes F are used. The H refers to how hard a pencil is, the B refers to its blackness and how soft it is, so that it can be smudged on the page, while the F refers to how sharp the pencil can be sharpened to. A number is also used, such as 2 or 3. The higher the number, the more of that particular attribute the pencil will be.

When sketching and shading, a soft pencil such as 4B is used. When doing a technical drawing such as an orthographic drawing, a 4H pencil may be used. An HB pencil is a blend of both hard and black.

Colouring pencils

Colouring pencils are useful for adding different shades of colour (tone) to a drawing. This is important in helping to make a sketch or drawing stand out from the page and also to give some idea of the materials used and the surface texture.

Many types of colouring pencils are available, the best being those that can be blended easily and have a bold range of colours. Variations in shades of colour are done simply by pressing harder.

Fine-line pens

Fine-line pens use fibre tips and are a popular tool for inking in lines and adding detail. They come is a variety of sizes, the most common being 0.3 mm, 0.5 mm and 0.7 mm. The size relates to the thickness of the line the pen creates. The thin, crisp line created can also be used when sketching, but it takes some skill to make this look effective. Fine-line pens are also good for giving a quality feel to written work in design folios.

Felt markers

Spirit-based felt markers are perhaps the most common media used by graphic designers. They are available in a wide range of sizes, colours, styles and prices. They are used to render a drawing and require practice to apply them effectively. Rendering flat areas by applying each pen stroke next to another without overlapping takes practice, and trying to fill in the gaps afterwards can be tricky. Colour tone can be built up by overlaying once a base layer has been applied.

Some bleeding of colour occurs on paper and card, so care must be taken not to colour right to the edge of an image or by using a colour mask. However, spirit pens do not soak paper as much as water-based felt pens.

Water-based felt markers are cheaper to buy and can be a very effective colouring media for covering small areas or when adding fine detail, like when creating lettering or outlining.

Having a set of basic felt markers to complement a set of colouring pencils is essential for any designer.

Technical pens

Technical pens create fine, uniform lines and tend to be used on detailed drawings like architectural plans and orthographic layouts. They normally use inks that are permanent and densely black, but other colours are available. The pens have special nibs and rechargeable cartridges, which ensure the ink flows uniformly, and they are available in standard sizes based on line width: 0.3 mm, 0.5 mm, 0.7 mm and 1mm. Cheaper, disposable pens are available but tend not to last as long.

A technical drawing

Airbrushes

Airbrushes use a low-pressure air supply to blow ink or special paint onto a surface. They are used primarily to colour render high-quality images as seen on film posters, record sleeves and artists' impression images.

An airbrush in action

Airbrushes are best used for rendering graduated tones, although flat areas of colour can also be achieved. Care and patience are the key to success, as producing a quality finish takes time with a lot of masking needed to avoid getting ink on the wrong areas.

Paints

Paints are used to colour render and offer a different quality to inks and colouring pencils. Many types are available, of which the following are the most common:

- Water colours: best used as a wash for creating a light base colour. Good for producing subtle colouring and graduation of colour.
- Acrylics: plastic-based paint available in bright, bold colours. Good for painting on different surfaces and can be watered down to create a colour stain.
- Enamels: good for painting models. Available in a wide range of colours and provide a tough finish.
- Gouache: a fairly expensive paint with a thick, creamy consistency. Good for producing areas of flat colour.

Coursework

Choose the most appropriate tools for the type of design work you are doing. Try to use a variety of media in your coursework as this will give your work more value.

Activities

1 Name the type of pencils you would use for sketching, technical drawing and shading.

2 Draw and render simple shapes using a range of different tools and equipment and evaluate the effect of each.

Summary

★ A wide range of tools and equipment are available when designing graphic products.

★ Select the most appropriate tool for the job, depending on what effect you are looking for.

Materials and components

Tools and equipment 2

In this chapter you will:

★ **learn about the different types of technical instruments, cutting tools and adhesives available to the graphic products designer.**

Technical instruments

Drawing boards

The simplest type of drawing board is bigger than an A3 sheet and has a flat, even surface with clean, square edges. A Tee square is then used to form a parallel motion, which slides up and down the side of the board. More expensive boards have an integral parallel motion and include paper clips and guidelines. By placing a set square onto the Tee square, various angles or parallel lines can be drawn.

Set squares

Set squares are triangular, clear, plastic instruments that are used to create lines at specific angles. One type has 30° and 60° angled sides and is used to produce isometric projections. The other main type is set at 45° and is used for oblique and orthographic projections.

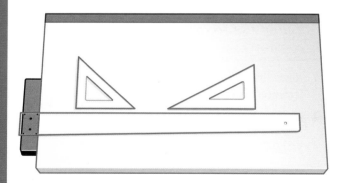

A drawing board with a set of set squares and a Tee square

Compasses and dividers

Compasses are used to draw circles and arcs. Always try to use a compass with a screw adjustment for greater accuracy. Attachments are available that allow fine-line pens to be used. More expensive compasses come with extension arms to allow large circles to be drawn.

Dividers are similar to compasses, but have two points and are used for measuring intersections between two points – useful when constructing geometric shapes.

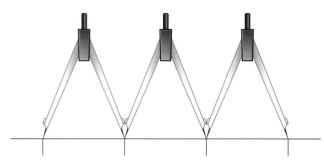

Dividing a line to measure equal spaces

Rulers and protractors

Rulers are the most basic tool used in graphics. They are used for measuring length and drawing straight lines. The best types are made from clear plastic and are 300 mm long with bevelled edges.

Protractors are used to measure angles and are designed to be used on a Tee square. Other circular angle measurers are available, which can also construct standard-sized circles.

French curves and circle templates

Circle templates are used to speed up the drawing of circles and ellipses. They are available in a wide range of sizes and, in the case of ellipses, all the standard drawing angles. French curves are plastic templates that have useful curves of varying radii, which can be rotated until the correct section of curve fits your drawing.

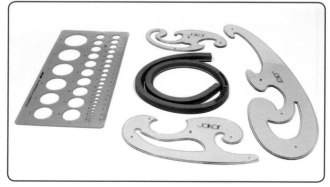

A selection of templates

Support equipment

Other useful drawing aids are lightboxes and photocopiers. Lightboxes have a semi-opaque glass surface, illuminated from below. This allows a drawn image to be traced easily onto another sheet without using tracing paper.

Photocopiers are excellent for copying pages, enlarging or reducing images and for cropping. Colour copiers also give a printed appearance to a piece of hand-rendered master artwork.

Cutting and shaping tools

Craft knives and scalpels

Craft knives are used mainly for cutting. They are available in many forms, but the best types have snap-off retractable blades. Scalpels are very sharp tools and are generally used for cutting fine detail into thin card. As with all cutting tools, safety is important. Always use a cutting mat and a safety rule.

Scissors

Basic safety scissors are good for general cutting of paper and thin card. Some scissors have special blades for producing patterns. Professional pattern-cutting scissors are very sharp, so care is needed when handling them.

Rotary cutters and compass cutters

These are used for cutting circles and arcs in thin card or paper. Compass cutters are better for smaller diameters on thin card, while rotary cutters are more heavy duty and can cut larger diameters on thicker card. Practice is needed when using them, as it is important not to try to cut through the card in one go – it is better to use light pressure and repeat the cut a few times. Always use on a cutting mat.

Adhesives

When modelling or constructing a product, adhesives need to be applied in a controlled and safe manner.
- PVA: used for gluing paper and card. Water-based and non-toxic.

- Epoxy resin: used for bonding metals and some plastics. Use in a well-ventilated area and wear safety goggles and gloves.
- Spray adhesives (Spray Mount): used for mounting paper onto card. Use in a well-ventilated area or a spray booth.
- Hot glue (used in glue guns): used to bond almost any material. Use a stand for the glue gun and keep hands away from the nozzle.
- Tape (masking, double-sided, etc): good for sticking parts together while modelling in card or paper.
- Adhesive film (as used in a laminating machine): useful for covering paper or card to give a wipe-clean surface. Care must be taken to ensure bubbles are not trapped when applying.
- Masking fluid: used to protect areas that do not require ink or paint. Most fluids are spirit-based and need to be applied in a well-ventilated area. Use a small brush to ensure accuracy when applying.

Activities

1 Draw simple geometric shapes, such as squares, hexagons and triangles, using appropriate technical instruments.

2 Explain how die cutters are used in the manufacture of a simple card package.

3 Produce a table showing what adhesives are used for different materials and what safety aspects need to be considered.

Summary

★ Technical instruments are used to produce accurate drawings by hand.

★ Different cutting tools are available for cutting different materials and care needs to be taken in selecting the most suitable type.

★ A wide range of adhesives is available to bond two surfaces together. Care needs to be taken in choosing the appropriate type.

Materials and components

1 The figure below shows a pet carrier box made from corrugated cardboard. The ink used is a smart ink.

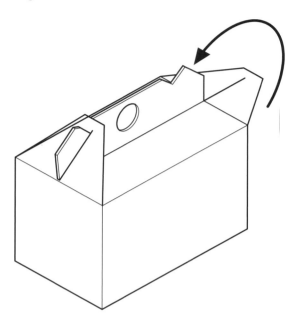

a Give two reasons why corrugated card is used for pet carrier boxes. Explain your answer. *(4 marks)*

b Give one disadvantage of using corrugated card for pet carrier boxes. Explain your answer. *(2 marks)*

c Explain how a thermochromic ink reacts. *(2 marks)*

d Give one other example of the use of thermochromic inks. *(1 mark)*

(AQA 2003)

2 The illustration below shows a scratch card that incorporates smart inks.

a Name two smart pigments used in printing inks. *(2 marks)*

b Explain what is meant by the term 'smart material'. *(2 marks)*

4

ICT: CAD/CAM

This section explains the various applications of ICT in the design and manufacture of graphic products. A wide range of different software types is featured, along with the main computer peripherals such as scanners, printers and CAM equipment.

What's in this section?

Using ICT

Information and communication technology (ICT) relates to how computers and other forms of technology can help to make us better informed and able to work more efficiently. ICT is not just about the Internet – it is about a wide range of different ways of communicating. Using ICT could help you improve the quality and accuracy of your graphic products coursework.

ICT in graphic design

Look at the design process model below. What follows are some suggestions on how ICT could help to improve the quality of your work.

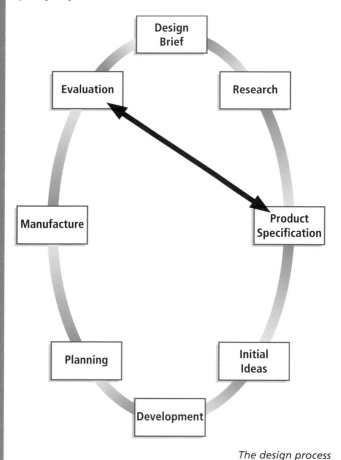

The design process

Research

- Use an Internet search engine to find out information about your project.
- Access websites directly.
- Send e-mails to companies to ask for information about their products.
- Visit virtual factories on the Internet to see how manufacturing is carried out in industry.

Design ideas

- Use a **digital camera** and photo editing software to change existing pictures.
- Use CAD software to create ideas quickly and easily. These can be rotated and modified in numerous ways.

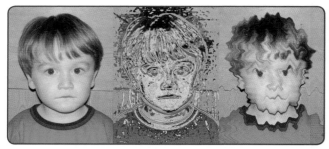

Use photo editing software to create interesting effects

Development

- Use **CAM** software to make a virtual model of your solution.
- Use a database or CD-ROM to find out more about the most appropriate materials for your design.

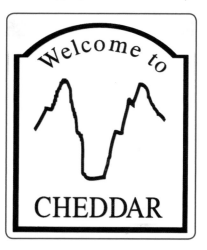

A simple model produced using a computer-controlled vinyl cutter

Final design

- Use a 3D **scanner** and cutter to manufacture your design from your high-quality prototype model.
- Use a DTP programme to produce 2D leaflets to advertise the product.

Example of an DVD case insert

Planning

- Use a spreadsheet to work out detailed costings of your product.
- Use layout software to create the production schedule or use flow chart software to generate a flow chart.

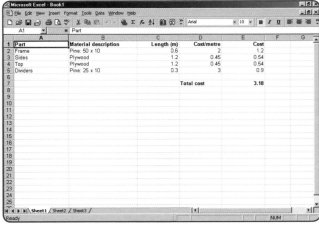

Spreadsheet programmes can help with budgets and costings

Making

- Use CAM software to make the final product, such as a computer-controlled **plotter cutter**.
- Use a computer-controlled plotter/cutter to make a point-of-sale display.

Evaluation

- Hold a video conference about your product.
- Send digital pictures taken using a digital camera by e-mail to companies and individuals for them to analyse.
- Show your ideas to a client or using a webcam linked to a computer.
- Use a word processing programme to write a detailed report about your product.
- Use a scanner to illustrate any changes made.

Coursework

Using ICT is an essential requirement for success at GCSE – you must make every effort to include it in your coursework.

Activity

Name three stages in the design process and, for each stage, explain how ICT may support the work of the designer.

Summary

★ Careful use of ICT will improve the quality of all your designing and making activities.

ICT: CAD/CAM

Digitising pictures

A student's CD cover design using scanned images

Scanners

In recent years, graphic designers have come to rely more and more on scanners in the design of graphic products.

A scanner is a device that creates an electronic map of a picture. This map is a made up of a series of dots or pixels. The quality of the picture is determined by how many dots there are per square millimetre. This is known as the resolution and the higher the resolution, the better the quality of the picture. Scanners are usually A3 or A4 size, making them ideal for design work.

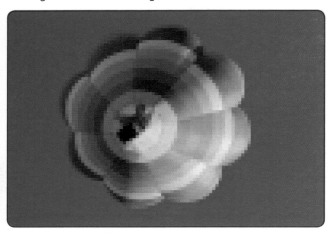

A scanner produces an electronic map of the image made up of a series of dots or pixels

High-resolution scanned colour images take up a lot of computer memory and are often too large to store on a floppy disk. Try to save your files using a compressed file format such as .jpg.

Using scanners

Scanners are particularly useful in design and technology projects because they allow you to add photographs and realistic pictures to your work. This helps you make high-quality graphic products that look like the real thing. Scanners also operate as colour photocopiers, so you can make copies of graphic work and include them in your design folders.

Digital cameras

Digital cameras are a cross between a normal camera and a scanner. You use them just like a normal camera, but instead of the images being captured on photographic film, they are saved digitally. Digital cameras have a small screen at the back of the camera that allows you to see the pictures once you have taken them. This means if you are not happy with your images, you can delete them and start again.

Once the pictures have been taken, they need to be transferred to a computer. Most digital cameras are connected to a computer using a cable. The digital camera acts like a separate hard disk, allowing you to view the pictures you have taken and insert them directly into the files you are working on.

Digital editing

When pictures have been scanned or uploaded to the computer, they are saved as digital images. These images can now be changed or edited using photo editing software. The most common forms of digital editing are:
• cropping: cutting an image down to the required size
• rotating: turning an image about a point or flipping it
• resizing: making the image larger or smaller.

In addition, the individual pixels can have their colours changed, or be deleted or modified in some way. Doing this will help you to create interesting graphic products.

Changing images and creating interest

Often pictures have minor flaws in them, such as 'red eye' caused by flash photography. These can be remedied easily using digital editing software.

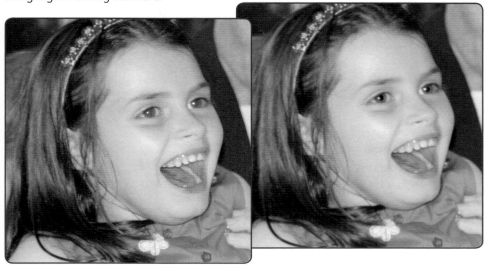

Digital editing software can remove 'red eye'

Once an image has been uploaded, all sorts of effects (called filters) can be applied to it. Adding effects such as twirls, distortions and perspective add interest and can form the basis of creative graphic product design. Look at how digital editing has changed the picture of the egg (below). It suddenly doesn't look so tasty does it?!

Would you eat this egg?

Activities

1. Give two reasons why scanners are popular with designers

2. Explain what is meant by the term 'digital editing'.

Summary

★ Scanners and digital cameras provide designers with the images for graphic product design.

★ Digital editing allows images to be changed and distorted to create interesting designs.

ICT: CAD/CAM

Using a digital camera

In this chapter you will:

★ **learn how to make the most of a digital camera in your graphic products coursework.**

Producing a drawing template

A digital camera can be a useful tool because it enables designers to produce underlays that help to improve the quality of drawings and sketches.

As part of a graphics project you may be required to carry out product analysis. The presentation of this activity always requires a picture of the object to be used. An object such as a car is a difficult product to draw well.

The first stage is to open the image taken by the digital camera into the digital editing software. The image should be cut away from the background. This is important so that a clear outline can be traced by the computer.

The next stage is to use the 'find the edges' facility on the digital editing software. This produces an outline of the image, which you can use for your own drawing.

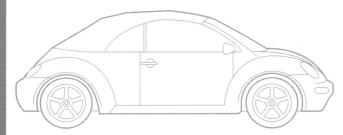

The car outline is produced

Once printed, the outline can be placed under your design sheet and the picture traced through. It is a good idea to use a light box so that the underlay is clear.

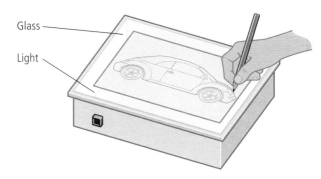

A light box enables photos or complex drawings to be traced

Alternatively, the digital editing software can be used for inserting a coloured background behind the image. This technique is particularly useful for producing a presentation drawing of your final design.

Interesting visual effects can be created

Producing high-quality graphic products

Images taken using a digital camera or downloaded from the Internet can be manipulated and combined with other images to create useful graphic products.

The following design project was given to a group of students on a graphic products course: 'Use photo editing software to produce a do not disturb sign.' The original pictures were downloaded form the Internet but high-quality graphic products can be produced easily and quickly using digital editing software. Alternatively, the pictures could have been scanned from a book or uploaded from a digital camera.

The first task was to create a door sign template.

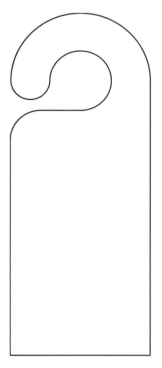

The door sign template

One of the manufacturing specification points for the door sign was that it should relate to a popular film or band. A range of images was selected.

The selected images

The final stage was to merge the chosen images with the door sign template.

The final sign

Once printed, the front and back images of the door template can be joined together with double-sided tape to produce a realistic graphic product.

Activity

Explain two ways in which digital cameras can be used in the design of graphic products.

Summary

★ High-quality graphic products can be produced easily and quickly using digital cameras.

★ Digital images from a camera or the Internet can be combined and manipulated to form high-quality graphic products.

ICT: CAD/CAM

Computer-aided design (CAD)

> **In this chapter you will:**
> ★ **learn about the common features of CAD software**
> ★ **how you can use CAD to produce accurate working drawings.**

Computers can make the work of the designer quicker and easier. As the name suggests, computer-aided design (CAD) is a computer software program that assists designers in their work.

Features of CAD

Most CAD software requires you to produce orthographic (2D) drawings. From 2D drawings, CAD programs will generate 3D views for you. However, some programs will also work the other way round and will produce fully detailed working drawings for you. These programs have a library of all the correct symbols, and will automatically add the dimensions to your work as you draw. As with any other drawing package, CAD software lets you fill areas with colour or hatched lines.

Using CAD

When you draw things by hand, whenever you make a mistake you have to rub it out and start again. Sometimes you need to change something halfway through a drawing.

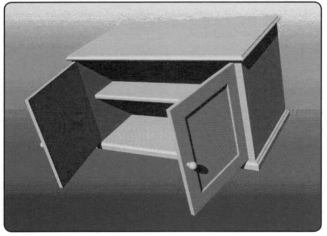

An object can be resized or rotated easily and quickly

All these things are time con suming and frustrating to the designer. With CAD, making changes is easy. Being able to rotate or duplicate an object are also useful features.

Designers use CAD in industry to view a model of an object. The image on a CAD screen is known as a wireframe model. This is because it looks as though it is made up lots of wires. Each line or wire follows the contour of the product, which helps to create the 3D shape. This virtual modelling is a major benefit of CAD software because it means that a product can be seen from all angles simply by rotating the image. A car designer, for example, can open and close doors on a car, change colours and wheel types – all at the touch of a mouse.

Making realistic models

CAD software such as Pro/DESKTOP enables designers to make the virtual model very realistic by adding different surface textures such as wood. This is known as surface modelling and helps you to get a better understanding of what the product will look like when produced.

Computers are used widely to model components and products on the screen, which means designs can be evaluated before the product is made.

Surface modelling

Working drawings

In your graphics coursework project, the most useful way of using CAD is to help you produce working drawings. A working drawing gives dimensions and all the details needed to make your designs (see page 30).

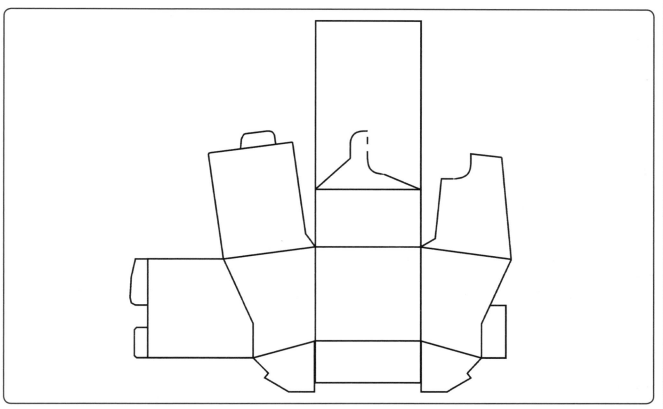

Working drawings save time and help you to produce accurate drawings

[Ic] Coursework

You could use CAD software such as Techsoft 2D Design or Pro/DESKTOP to produce an accurate working drawing of your design idea.

Activities

1 Name three objects that have been designed with the used of CAD.

2 Explain the advantages and disadvantages to the designer of using CAD when designing.

Summary

★ CAD software is not a replacement for the designer – it does not come up with the ideas.

★ CAD is a useful tool for the designer – it provides him with the means for modelling his ideas.

★ **Computer modelling** means that ideas can be tested for appearance, size and functional details without having to physically make anything.

★ CAD saves time and helps to ensure accuracy and precision.

ICT: CAD/CAM

In this chapter you will:

★ **learn how CAM is used to manufacture accurate products in quantity.**

Computers help designers to design products and have the advantage of being quicker and more accurate than humans. The same is true for making products. Computers are fitted to machines to control their movements. The computer is given a set of instructions in the form of a computer program, which tells it exactly what to do. Unlike humans, computers do not need a break and can work 24 hours a day, seven days a week.

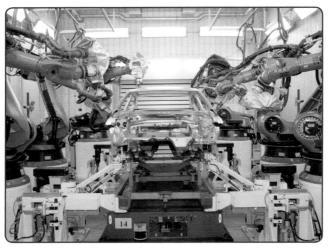

The use of CAM in production

In industry, computers control many manufacturing processes. Robots can do dangerous tasks, unsafe for humans. With the help of CAM, production is now fast. Large motor manufacturers such as Volkswagen can produce a complete car in less than 24 hours.

CAM and graphic products

CAM is widely used for the manufacture of graphic products. The starting point for this process is the final design or working drawing. The device that is going to make the product is connected to the computer by a cable and set up with the correct materials. The CAM machine is able to understand the commands from the computer and follows these instructions.

CAM cutters

Vinyl can be cut out accurately and used to make signs using a CAM cutter. A CAM cutter works by using a knife to follow the coordinates of a line drawing produced on a computer. As the drawing is plotted, the knife cuts the outline of the shape. When finished, the self-adhesive vinyl is peeled off the backing and can then be applied to signs or other objects.

Vinyl lettering produced using a CAM cutter is applied to the point-of-sale display

CAM cutters work from coordinates, so they cannot be using for cutting a scanned image or digital photo. This is because scanned images are produced as a series of dots known as a bitmap.

Some CAM machines use a rotating cutter rather than a static knife. These are called router or milling machines. Large CAM milling machines are used widely in industry but they are very expensive. Small CAM machines can be useful as engraving tools. Designs can be cut out of solid plastic and used as plaques or logos on larger products.

Laser cutters

Laser cutters use high-intensity laser light to accurately cut out paper, plastic, wood and metal. While laser cutters are relatively expensive, they cut the material so cleanly and precisely that no additional work is required. Because they can cut out intricate shapes, they are useful for producing press formes.

Embroidery

Graphic product design often involves designing logos for companies and organisations. One way that these designs are used is on uniforms. Logos can be reproduced on clothing using computer-controlled sewing machines.

Computer-controlled sewing machines are useful for transferring logos onto clothes

These sewing machines are able to work from scanned images of designs. The machine is set up with the right colour cotton and the design produced.

A wide range of graphic products can be produced using CAM

Coursework

CAM machines enable you to produce high-quality, accurate products in a range of materials.

Activity

List three advantages to the manufacturer of using CAM.

Summary

★ CAM enables manufacturers to produce high-quality products quickly and accurately.

★ New CAM machines, such as laser cutters, enable highly accurate cutting out of materials such as card, thin plastic and wood.

ICT: CAD/CAM

Using the Internet

A whole new language has developed since the dawn of the Internet. Words like cyberspace, e-mail and search engine are now part of our everyday vocabulary. The Internet is a network of interconnected computers around the world. This new world where people are linked together electronically is called cyberspace.

Using the Internet

All you need to connect to the Internet is a computer, a modem and a telephone line. A modem is an electronic device that converts the digital signals from the computer into sound signals that can then be sent down the telephone line. A modem works in reverse when it receives signals from other computers. A wide range of resources can be found on the Internet. These can be invaluable when you need to carry out research for your graphic projects. However, examiners will give no credit to students who merely download information and do nothing with it. Make sure that any information gained is carefully selected and analysed before being included in your design folder. Also ensure you include details of the source of your information.

Websites

Each company or individual who sets up a website on the Internet has an address. Searching for a particular address will lead you to a website.

Finding a website

The Cabaret Mechanical Theatre is an interesting website full of mechanical moving toys. To access the Cabaret Mechanical Theatre site, please go to www.heinemann. co.uk/hotlinks, insert the express code 3457P and click on the website name.

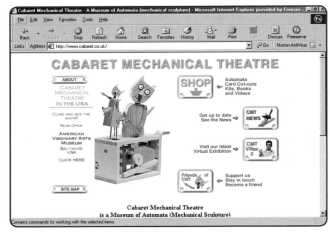

The Cabaret Mechanical Theatre website

The website is full of information about mechanical toys and other attractions. It is split into sections to enable you to find your way around more easily. The site allows people to find out about mechanical sculptures and buy products online.

The design of websites like this must be clear and simple. Just like a book, they must have an index, clear headings and simple-to-follow instructions. They must also be interesting and informative. The best websites make you feel as though you are virtually there.

Designing a web page

In the same way that graphic designers have traditionally designed leaflets, brochures and advertising campaigns, they are now frequently called upon to design web pages. Web page design is different to book or leaflet design. Pages do not have to fit into a particular grid or size, they can be as long or as short as necessary, and there is no limit on the number of pictures or images used.

Design in action

When designing a website, it is important to remember that everyone will see the site slightly differently. This is because the quality of computer monitors varies enormously. Therefore, unlike a book – which is the same for all readers – small, complex images and text may not work.

Reading text on a computer screen can also be difficult. The choice of text, its size and colour are important to the

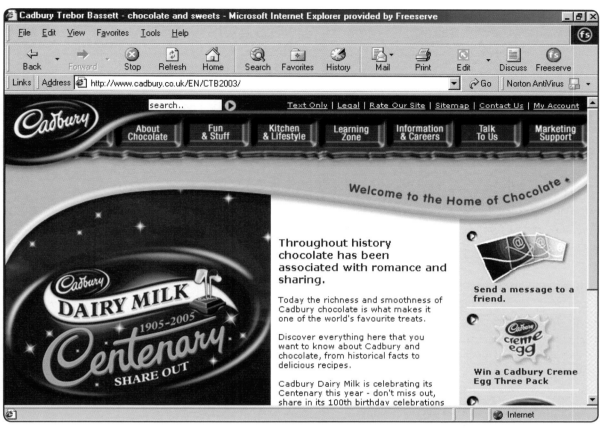

The Cadbury website

design. Good website design needs to attract readers and provide information in a clear and logical way.

Many websites incorporate a Flash media image to attract the reader. Flash is a software program that creates animated images – this grabs the reader's attention and helps to make a website inviting. Another key feature of good website design is the layout. Headings are usually limited to reduce clutter. Devices such as drop-down menus and pop-ups enable sub-headings to be hidden.

Unlike a book, which is printed and then rarely changed, a web page should be updated constantly. Design is only the start.

[ic] Coursework

Website design is a popular choice of project for GCSE graphic products students. However, it does not meet the exam board's requirement because it is not a 3D product.

Activities

1. Log on to the Internet and visit your favourite websites. For each site, make a list of the features of the design that make it visually interesting. Consider the use of colour, images such as logos, the size and style of typefaces and how easy the site is to use.

2. Explain the meaning of the following terms.
   a E-mail.   d Search engine.
   b World Wide Web.   e Broadband.
   c Modem.

3. List three ways that the Internet can be used in your GCSE coursework.

Summary

★ The Internet can be a valuable source of information for your design and technology project.

ICT: CAD/CAM

1 A charity shop sells a variety of veterinary collars. The collars are cut from 1 mm thick flexible polythene sheet. The surface development (net) of a similar collar is shown below.

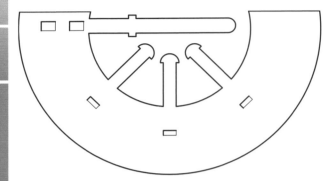

You have been asked to make 25 collars in your school.

  a Which scale of production should be used?

   i One-off

   ii Batch

   iii Mass

   iv Continuous   *(1 mark)*

  b Simple decoration can be added to the plain white plastic collar with the addition of stickers cut out of self-adhesive vinyl sheet. A CAM system is to be used to cut out the designs.

   i What do the letters CAM stand for? *(2 marks)*

   ii Give one advantage of using computer systems for multiple production. *(2 marks)*

2 a What does CAD stand for?   *(1 mark)*

  b What does CAM stand for?   *(1 mark)*

  c Give two advantages of using CAD for the design of packaging. *(2 marks)*

  d Explain how CAM can be used in the production of press formes used for die cutting the packaging nets. *(3 marks)*

  e Describe two implications in a design and manufacturing company of relying on the use of computers. *(4 marks)*

Systems and control

This section covers how systems and control are used in the design and manufacture of a graphic product. It includes how systems can be used to control the manufacturing process so that quality is achieved for one-off manufacture in school and also for large-scale production in industry. It also looks at systems that can be used to control mechanical movement in pop-up cards or similar products. It is important to include systems and control throughout the whole design process, especially in your coursework.

What's in this section?

★ **5.1** Safety: Risks and hazards

★ **5.2** Open loop and closed loop systems

★ **5.3** Flow charts

★ **5.4** Sequence illustrations and schematic maps

★ **5.5** Comparing school production to commercial production

★ **5.6** Quality systems

★ **5.7** Mechanical systems

★ **5.8** Paper engineering

Safety: Risks and hazards

In this chapter you will:

★ **learn how to recognise hazards**

★ **learn how to assess risks**

★ **learn how to recognise signs and symbols and how to take steps to control risks.**

Hazards

A hazard is something that could potentially harm someone. Being able to recognise hazards in everyday life is probably the single most important life skill we need to know. We learn from an early age that certain things could harm us and so we develop an awareness of potential hazards.

Some commercial products like craft knives can be potentially hazardous for everyone, but some groups such as the elderly, young children and disabled people can be particularly at risk.

When we design a product for other people to use, it is important that it is safe. This may seem obvious, but many products have been known to be unsafe. Typical examples include children's toys where the eyes have not been secured properly.

Childrens toys must be safe

Safety is also a major issue when using tools and equipment. Some tools require specific safety controls otherwise they could cause harm when being used. For example, a simple craft knife used correctly is a safe tool. However, if the knife is used without a safety rule or cutting mat, there is a higher risk of injury. Many tools need to be used in conjunction with another piece of equipment to minimise the risk of injury.

Many tools have built-in safety features, such as a craft knife with a retractable blade. Safety considerations often influence the design of craft tools. For example, if the handle of a tool is designed to be easy and comfortable to use, this will reduce the risk of an accident happening.

The table on the next page outlines a number of risks and hazards and advises on how to control the risk.

Workspaces

Machinery and workbenches need to be placed in appropriate positions so that there is enough space for people to use them safely. They should be positioned so that related processes in a manufacturing system are close together. This prevents excessive movement between each workstation and also helps to reduce employee stress.

HSE and BSI

The Health and Safety Executive (HSE) is responsible for ensuring that all workplace environments, such as schools, factories and offices, are safe places for people to work. It also inspects premises to check that there is no breach of health and safety laws. It has the power to close down a workplace if it thinks unsafe working practices are taking place.

The British Standards Institute (BSI) produces publications detailing a range of standards that apply to almost every area of human activity. For example, the British Standard kite mark is the UK's most recognised product certification mark. It is visible proof that the product is high quality and meets a published specification.

Safety signs and symbols

Safety signs identify hazards and are designed to be easy to understand. Different colours are used to identify different categories of signs:

- Red signs with a white background are prohibition signs – they are 'do not' signs.
- Blue signs with a white background are mandatory signs – they are 'must do' signs.

- Yellow signs are warning signs.
- Green signs are safety signs.

Safety posters are often used to illustrate safe working practices and can be important in reminding people of their responsibilities as well as any potential hazards.

Safety posters illustrate safe working practices

Activities

1 Design a safety poster for use in a school workshop.

2 What is the role of an HSE inspector?

Summary

★ It is important to assess the risks of using certain tools and equipment and to understand how to minimise them.

★ The HSE is responsible for safety in the workplace.

★ BSI 4163 is the health and safety standard for use in schools.

★ Signs and symbols use certain colours to give signs meaning.

Risk/hazard	Controlling the risk
General	
Equipment not working	Check equipment before use
Working on your own	Ensure someone else, ideally a teacher, is present
Bags and equipment on the floor	Move to a safe place
An accident happens	Stop and inform a teacher
Using machinery	
Cutting tools are blunt	Ask for them to be sharpened by a teacher or technician – never use a blunt tool
Material not held securely	Use a vice or clamp
Machine guards not working properly	Inform a teacher – never use a machine without a guard
Long hair and loose clothing	Tie back hair and roll up sleeves or tighten protective clothing
Changing a tool	Switch off machine at isolator switch
Using adhesives	
Using a glue gun	Avoid touching the nozzle and use a gun stand
Using Spray Mount	Use a spray booth
Using an acrylic cement	Wear eye protection and gloves, and use in a well-ventilated area
Using hand-held cutting tools	
Using a scalpel or craft knife	Ensure the blade is sharp, and keep the blade tight against the safety rule as you cut the material
Using a coping saw	Check the blade is set correctly and hold your work in a vice
Using computer equipment	
Headache/eye strain	Check the monitor is set up correctly and take a break every 20 minutes
Backache/repetitive strain injury	Check the stool is set correctly and that the keyboard height is comfortable
Air pollutants	
Poisonous gases caused by a hot wire cutte	Ensure the wire is at the correct temperature and use fume extraction
Dust in the air	Use dust extraction and/or dust guard

Risks and hazards

Systems and control

What is a system?

A system is a number of interacting elements that work together in a sequence to make something happen. All the stages together make up the system. These stages are:

• input: an instruction or force is applied
• process: the activity generated by the input
• output: the end result or outcome.

Systems are everywhere around us – almost every organisation has a system central to its management and operation, otherwise all the separate parts of the organisation would function in an uncoordinated way, resulting in poor performance.

Types of system

There are a number of different types of systems:

• natural systems: such as the weather and ecosystems
• design systems (using mechanical/electronic machinery): such as mobile phone communication networks or a printing machine
• human activity systems: such as working to a timetable.

Open loop systems

An open loop system is controlled manually. Usually it is a simple linear process. Look at the example below illustrating the use a craft knife to cut a piece of card.

In this type of system, the operator controls what happens next and, if adjustments are needed, he makes changes (feedback) as and when necessary. For example, if the straight edge is not aligned correctly, the operator would change it. An industrial example of an open loop system

INPUT	**PROCESS**	**OUTPUT**
The operator slides the craft knife along the edge of a saftey rule	The craft knife cuts through the card	The piece of card is cut in two

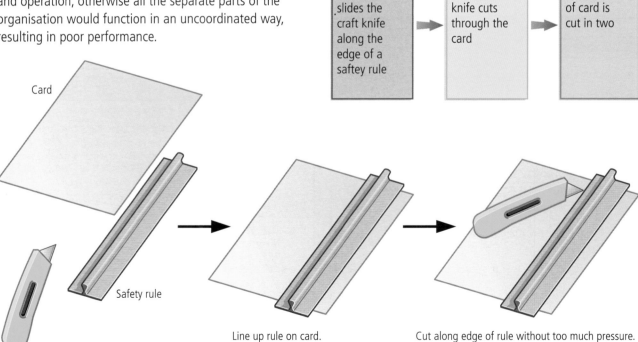

Card

Safety rule

Knife

Line up rule on card.
Press rule down onto card

Cut along edge of rule without too much pressure.
Repeat carefully until cut through

An open loop system

would be in the manufacture of arts and craft products, greetings cards, etc.

The means by which the inputs or processes are changed are called controls. The success of a system is judged on how well it transforms its inputs into outputs, and how well the feedback and control elements prevent problems occurring that might stop the system from working.

Closed loop systems

A closed loop system is normally controlled automatically and is monitored by either a machine or a computer. Closed loop systems employ feedback from sensors in the system, which tell the machine or device what to do next. Most manufacturing machines used in the graphics industry use closed loop systems.

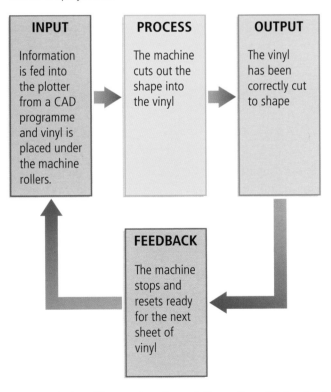

A closed loop system for a plotter cutter with feedback

Plotter cutters

When a product such as a vinyl label is to be cut out using a plotter cutter such as a CAMM1, the machine has built-in sensors to control and monitor such things as cutter pressure and the size of vinyl being used. A computer-generated drawing, designed using CAD, is downloaded to the machine and a set of machine codes are made. These codes control the movement of the cutter head and the rollers that move the vinyl. When all is set, the machine will run through its cycle until the label is made. Feedback occurs in two ways:

- The machine moves the cutting head over towards the vinyl and momentarily stops to register that the vinyl is there and that it is in the correct place. This information is relayed back to the control system and, if it is OK, the cutter will carry on. If an error occurs, it will stop so that a correction can be made.
- When the process is complete and a successful outcome has been produced, the machine stops and resets itself ready for the next sheet of vinyl to be cut.

Activities

1. Draw an open loop system for using a trimmer to cut card.
2. Draw a closed loop system (including feedback) for cutting and folding a piece of card into a cube.
3. Explain the differences between open loop and closed loop systems.

Summary

★ A system involves three stages: input, process and output.

★ Feedback is used to control what happens next in a system.

★ An open loop system is controlled manually – it has no automatic feedback to control output.

★ A closed loop system has automatic feedback control to monitor the output.

★ Closed loop systems are used by professional manufacturers because of the rate and ease of production.

Systems and control

Flow charts

A flow chart is a method of illustrating a sequence of operations when doing a task, like when manufacturing a product or understanding quality control procedures. Flow charts use standardised symbols and arrows to show the direction of flow.

 Terminal — This indicates the start and finish of the process

Process — This represents the process involved

Decision — This represents a decision to be made or a switching of operation

Input/ouput — This is used to represent adding (input) something or removing (output) something

 Adjust — This is used to represent when an adjustment to a process is needed

Flow chart symbols

A simple flow chart showing the process of having a bath

This is a simplistic flow chart and could be far more detailed. It does not allow for checking how hot the water is or whether the bath is filled up enough. For this we need to use feedback.

Feedback loops

Whenever a decision is made that will result in a yes or no answer, a loop is put into the system. Depending on the answer given, the flow may either continue straight on or take the route of the feedback loop to the previous stage. If the feedback loop is taken, an adjustment must be made before asking the question again.

The example on the next page shows how decision symbols are used to create questions. A yes answer leads to an adjust symbol with an arrow back to the previous point, while a no answer means the flow chart carries on.

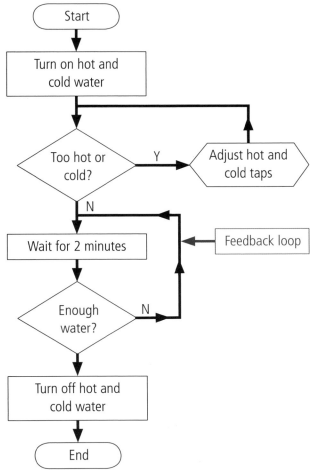

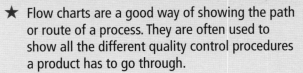

A flow chart with feedback loops

To include even more detail, an input/output symbol could be used to include adding some bubble bath. Where do you think this symbol should go? Will it need any adjustment?

Creating flow charts

- The layout should be clear – draft your flow chart first and make adjustments until it looks correct.
- Keep the symbol proportions consistent.
- Avoid crossing lines if you can.
- Use arrows to indicate the direction of flow.
- A vertical chart starts at the top.
- A horizontal chart starts at the left-hand side.

Flow charts can be produced easily using a computer – wordprocessing packages like Microsoft Word include built-in flow chart software. Specific software is also available to make creating flow charts straightfoward.

Ic Coursework

Flow charts are a useful way of producing your plan for production.

Activities

1 Draw a flow chart for putting someone's contact details into a mobile phone.

2 Explain the meaning and function of a feedback loop.

Summary

★ Flow charts are a good way of showing the path or route of a process. They are often used to show all the different quality control procedures a product has to go through.

★ Flow charts use standard symbols, which are recognised easily.

★ Feedback loops allow for adjustments to be made so that quality can be maintained.

★ There are rules to follow when creating flow charts.

5.4 Sequence illustrations and schematic maps

Sequence illustrations

Sequence illustrations use a series of drawings to show each step in the process of making or assembling a product or carrying out a task. Good examples are found in self-assembly flat-packed furniture. Companies like IKEA and MFI produce a range of products that can be put together at home. All the fixings are included, as well as an instruction sheet.

When drawing sequence illustrations, it is important to make sure your diagrams are clear and easy to understand. Here are some points to bear in mind:

- Use a fine-line pen to produce the outline of the product or part being explained – do not render the shape.
- Make sure the drawings are not too small.
- Always draw them in 3D – use a standard method like isometric.
- Instructions should be short and concise – use bullet points.
- Use arrows to point to various parts that need to be highlighted.
- Make sure it is obvious which drawing comes next in the sequence – number each stage or put it in a box.
- Get someone else to read through your work – can they follow the sequence and do the task without needing further instructions?

A flat-pack product

Schematic maps

Schematic maps mean drawing a complex route as a straight line. A good example of a schematic map is the London Underground map, which shows all the tube lines and stations linked together in a series of straight lines. The map is easy to understand even though the actual layout of the stations and lines do appear in real life where they do on the map.

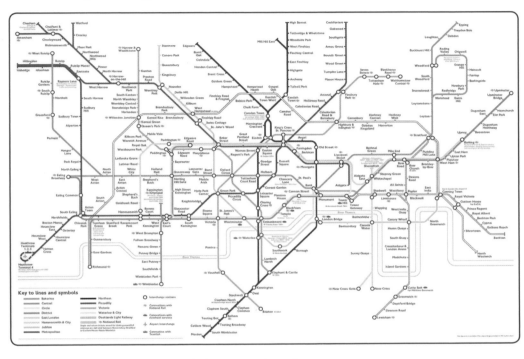

The London Underground map is a schematic map

A simple schematic map is shown below. Note that all landmarks are shown along the route and the distance between each one gives some idea of the actual relative distance.

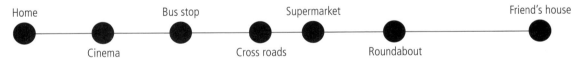

A schematic map showing the route from home to a friend's house

Activities

1   Produce a sequence illustration showing how to make a cup of tea.

2   Produce a schematic map of the route from your house to a friend's house, showing appropriate landmarks on the way.

Summary

★ Sequence illustrations are good at communicating a set of instructions in a graphical, easy-to-follow way.

★ Sequence illustrations have clear, step-by-step instructions.

★ Schematic maps simplify a route into a straight line.

Systems and control

5.5 Comparing school production to commercial production

In this chapter you will:
★ **learn about the differences between methods of production in school and commercial production.**

Quantity vs. one-off

Commercial products are usually manufactured in quantities greater than one, whereas in school products are usually manufactured as **one-off production**. However, this must not be a distraction from the focus on designing for manufacture in quantity – a requirement for coursework.

The methods and materials used for **batch production** vary considerably from those normally available in school. Also, the logical order of how a product is made can be very different when comparing one-off manufacture with high-quantity production.

Using the example of breakfast cereal packaging, you will examine the differences between how you would manufacture the product in school and the methods of a commercial manufacturer.

Manufacturing in school

A simple net development for a piece of breakfast cereal packaging is to be manufactured as a one-off in a school workshop. The first step in the process is to check what resources are likely to be available before starting to plan the sequence of manufacture.

CAD/CAM is becoming available in an increasing number of schools and this gives students the ability to mimic manufacturing in industry, albeit in small production quantities. Therefore, two main methods of production are available:
• manufacture by hand
• manufacture using CAD/CAM.

Manufacture by hand

• Draw the net development using a 4H pencil and a straight edge, or a high-quality ruler. Measure accurately.

• Draw the outline of the lettering using appropriate techniques such as stencils and pencils.
• Colour render the background colours and lettering outline using appropriate techniques and equipment: colouring pencils, marker pens, fine-line pens, paints, air brush, etc.
• Turn the net over and produce fold lines (indicated by dotted lines) using a straight edge and an old ballpoint pen on a cutting mat.
• Cut the outline of the net using a safety rule and craft knife. Always cut from the inside of a corner to the outside.
• Fold the net along the fold lines using a ruler as a guide.
• Apply glue to the tabs and assemble the net into the package form.

Manufacture using CAD/CAM

• Draw the net development and apply crop marks using a suitable software package such as Techsoft 2D Design or Pro/DESKTOP.
• Add colour rendering and graphic imagery to the net using a suitable software package. The net could be imported into another software programme such as CorelDRAW.
• Apply lay planning if you are aiming to print out more than one net.
• Print the net development onto a suitably sized piece of card.
• Set up the CAM plotter cutter with the correct tool and programme sequence.
• Line up the crop marks and registration points on the plotter cutter, clamp the card in place and set the machine to start.
• Unclamp the card from the cutter and reset the machine.
• Fold, glue and assemble the net.

CAD/CAM alters the method of manufacture by making the drawing element easier without the need for pencils, rulers and straight edges. It also allows changes to be made quickly if problems arise. Accuracy is also likely to be improved.

Industrial manufacture

In industry, packages are manufactured by printing and folding machines. The whole process is more **automated** and, while some of the methods used can be reproduced in school, the systems involved incorporate many more control elements to ensure quality because the manufacturing process is more complex. Machinery is also expensive, but a manufacturer needs only to employ a few people to run them.

A typical piece of packaging such as a cereal box will be batch produced in quantities in excess of 50,000, so **quality control** is especially important. Any errors in production could mean added costs and lost profits.

The designers of the cereal packet will make decisions early on in the design process about how many products will be made at any one time. The type of production method used has major implications on the cost of the product and sometimes the design. Also, as the **scale of production** increases, the logical order of how a product is made can change, especially compared with one-off production.

Commercial production

Look at the stages in commercial production of a simple package and compare this to the manufacturing in school example. The main differences are:
- increase in speed of production
- increase in number of packages produced per unit of time
- higher-quality materials used
- consistency in quality
- lower overall cost per package when a large production run is finished.

Activities

1 Imagine you have been asked to manufacture a simple package for a chocolate company. Draw a series of diagrams to represent the stages of production for manufacturing a one-off prototype and for batch producing in large quantities.

2 Explain how changes in the scale of production affect the methods of production.

Summary

★ Manufacturing in school tends to be more labour intensive and requires greater use of craft tools.

★ Manufacturing in industry tends to be more automated with machines able to do more than one process at a time.

★ The logical order of work changes as the scale of production increases.

★ Fewer employees are needed to create the same amount of products when manufactured in industry.

In this chapter you will:
★ learn about the difference between **quality assurance** and **quality control**
★ learn how the quality of products is checked during manufacture.

What is quality?

Manufacturers need to ensure that all the products they make are of an acceptable quality. Quality is about achieving the highest possible standards in all design and manufacturing activities.

The first step to ensure quality in the manufacture of a product is to define what standard or level of quality is required. To help do this, it is useful to think about how and why. For example, the acceptable level of quality for newspaper print is different from the quality expected from a glossy magazine or coffee-table book. Newspapers have a short shelf life as they are produced daily and discarded

in a short time. They also cost little to buy. Therefore, the materials and processes used take this into account. The expected level of quality for a glossy magazine is much higher, with the text and pictures being crisper. Also, the paper used is less absorbent and feels glossy.

Quality assurance

If a manufacturer can make a product in the most cost-effective way and ensure that the quality defined in the product specification is met, both the consumer and the manufacturer will be satisfied. Therefore, a quality product could be defined as being good value for money – think about how you choose which product to buy and how much you are prepared to pay. What quality level do you expect? All these factors need to be considered.

Quality assurance (QA) is a set of standards, systems and procedures written by a manufacturer or company to ensure high standards of quality are achieved during every stage of design and manufacture. Usually a company manual is produced that contains all the relevant details. European quality assurance standards are awarded to companies who can prove they have quality systems in place that ensure quality. Many companies purchase materials or components only from organisations who have met the basic standards.

Many companies use a management philosophy called **total quality management (TQM)**. This is an approach where the human and physical resources of an organisation are maximised in the most cost-effective way to meet the needs of the consumer and the community. One example of this is cell manufacture. A small group of workers (known as a cell) manufacture a product or component in its entirety and are given the responsibility for its manufacture and quality. Cells are also encouraged to use their own ideas in improving manufacturing methods and processes. The aim of this is to make everyone feel valued, no matter what job they are doing.

Quality control

Quality control involves checking to ensure a product or operational process has being carried out correctly and that the required quality standard, set by the customer, has been met. There are numerous methods for checking quality,

A close-up view of a newspaper and a glossy magazine showing surface texture and print

depending on the product or process being assessed. In the manufacture of graphic products, checks might be made on the following:

- size: does the product fall within the **tolerances** set as a standard?
- colour: does the product match the colour specification for tone, density and hue?
- alignment: do the combinations of colours used, **embossed** features and folds all line up?

Printed graphic products use a series of printers' marks for quality. Normally a set of **proofs** are made. These are like a master copy of the finished item, which are used to check against. Colour bars and registration marks are used to check the quality of the finished product. Printers sometimes view proofs using a magnifying glass and a light box to check the detail closely. Any errors in quality will

mean the machine needs to be adjusted before production can begin.

In practice, quality control would be very time consuming if every product, especially those being batch produced, were individually inspected. In most systems, a sample such as one in every 100 is inspected. The sample is checked to see how close it is to the tolerance limit and a record of the results inserted into a graph. If the product falls within acceptable limits, production continues. By using sampling, manufacturers can usually predict when adjustments need to made.

mark to ensure black ink is printing at the right density

colour bar to take readings to ensure colour density is consistent throughout book

crop marks to show where pages should be trimmed

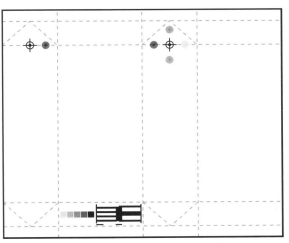

The printers' marks are used to check quality

bleed to allow tolerance in the trim

file name

registration marks to line up the four colour separations exactly

A proof of a book

5.6 Quality systems

In this chapter you will:
★ learn about the difference between quality assurance and quality control
★ learn how the quality of products is checked during manufacture.

What is quality?

Quality assurance

Quality control

the Royal Opera House

egg

A close-up view of a newspaper and a glossy magazine showing surface texture and print

88 Graphic Products

Activities

1 Investigate printers' marks such as colour bars, registration marks and crop marks on a variety of printed products.

2 Explain why quality is important both to the consumer and to the manufacturer.

Summary

★ Quality assurance is the set of procedures put in place by a manufacturer to ensure quality.

★ Quality control involves checking the product at various stages of production to ensure quality.

★ Printers use crop marks, colour bars and registration marks to check proofs.

Systems and control

In this chapter you will:

★ learn about different kinds of motion

★ learn the principles of simple mechanisms such as levers, cranks and sliders, linkages and cams.

Most graphic products are static but some are designed for movement. Novelty products such as pop-up cards, mechanised models and point-of-sale displays are becoming increasingly popular to advertise manufactured goods.

Types of movement

A mechanism is a system that creates or changes the type of movement of an object. The movement of an object is governed by four main types of motion.

Linear motion

Movement is in one direction in a straight line.

Linear motion occurs when a cash register till opens

Rotary motion

Movement is in a circular manner, like a wheel on a car.

Rotary motion occurs in a circular fashion

Reciprocating motion

Moving backwards and forwards or upwards and downwards.

Reciprocating motion occurs when a sewing machine needle moves up and down

Oscillating motion

Movement that is swinging from side to side.

Oscillating motion occurs when a child plays on a swing

Types of mechanism

To create mechanical movement in graphic products, there are a number of basic mechanisms that can be used.

Levers

These devices are useful as they can amplify or reduce movement depending on where the pivot point is. A simple class-one lever is shown below. If the pivot point is moved left or right, the amount of movement created at point A compared with point B will either increase or decrease.

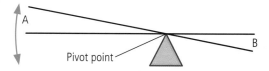

A class-one lever

Cranks and sliders

A crank is a lever that moves in a circular motion. You find them on bicycles as pedal cranks. They are often used in conjunction with a slider to convert rotary motion into reciprocating motion.

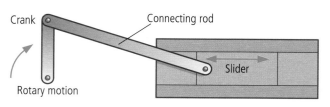

A crank and slider

Linkages

A linkage transmits force and motion from one point to another, sometimes changing the force and/or the direction of motion. A linkage is made up of a series of interconnecting struts and levers. The main types are shown below.

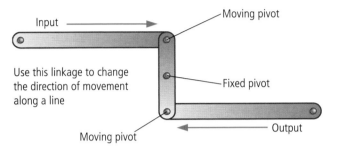

Input — Moving pivot

Use this linkage to change the direction of movement along a line

Fixed pivot

Moving pivot — Output

Reverse motion linkage

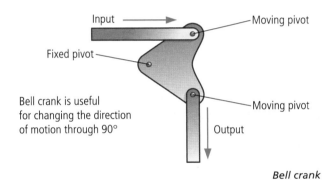

Input — Moving pivot

Fixed pivot

Bell crank is useful for changing the direction of motion through 90°

Moving pivot — Output

Bell crank

Note that in both types of linkages, if the fixed pivot point is moved nearer to one of the moving pivot points, there will be a change in the amount of movement between the input and output.

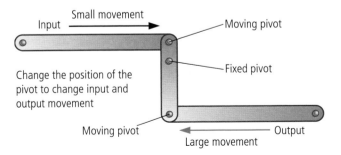

Small movement
Input — Moving pivot

Change the position of the pivot to change input and output movement

Fixed pivot

Moving pivot — Output
Large movement

The pivot point is moved

Cams

Cams are circular devices that are normally used to change circular motion into reciprocating motion. When a cam rotates, the follower rises and falls every time the drive shaft turns one full revolution.

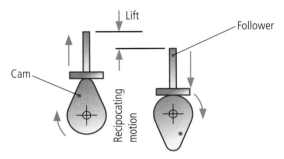

Lift

Follower

Cam

Reciprocating motion

A cam and follower

Different types of cam give different types of reciprocating motion. Look at the examples below and try to work out which type of reciprocating motions occurs.

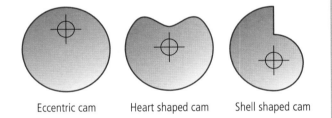

Eccentric cam   Heart shaped cam   Shell shaped cam

Eccentric, heart-shaped and shell-shaped cams

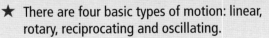

Activities

1 Create a symbol to represent each of the four types of motion.

2 Suggest a graphic product that could incorporate a simple mechanism.

Summary

★ There are four basic types of motion: linear, rotary, reciprocating and oscillating.

★ Mechanisms create or change the type of motion of an object.

★ There are many types of mechanism such as cams, levers and linkages.

Systems and control

In this chapter you will:

★ **learn how simple paper mechanisms can be used to create impact and appeal to cards and books**

★ **learn how some of the basic pop-up mechanisms work.**

Creating pop-ups is an interesting and exciting way of producing graphic products. Pop-ups use paper engineering techniques to help bring stories to life and create impact and appeal. Some of the most fascinating examples of pop-ups are found in children's books and birthday cards.

Pop-up cards use a variety of different mechanisms to create movement. The most common types are V-folds, parallelograms and pivoting motion.

V-folds

A V-fold is a commonly used mechanism in pop-up cards. It is simple to produce, although accuracy is required.

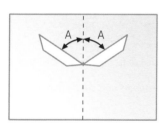

This example has the fold facing you as the card opens to give a dramatic effect. It also has a smaller fold in the foreground for added impact.

Making a V-fold

1 Make sure the two angles marked A are exactly the same. They should be less than 90° but more than 60° otherwise it will not fold properly.

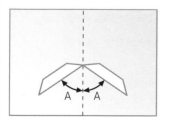

2 Cut out the card shape and use a ballpoint pen to score along the fold lines.

3 As the card is folded, the pop-up folds down and towards you. Make sure you position the V-fold near to the top of the card, otherwise it will stick out of the bottom when closed.

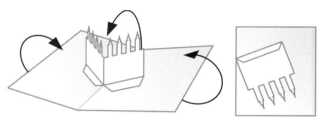

Parallelograms

This mechanism was one of the first to be used in pop-up cards. It is also one of the simplest to make. Parallelograms provide a solid-looking 3D form when the card is opened, and, by adding multiple layers, an impression of depth can be created.

A basic parallelogram

Making a parallelogram

When a parallelogram pop-up is unfolded, the shape should form a rectangle. In order for the parallelogram to fold up correctly, the two glue tab areas must lie parallel to the spine of the card.

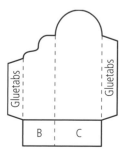

To make sure the pop-up does not stick out when the card is closed, make sure measurement A is longer than B and that measurement D is longer than C.

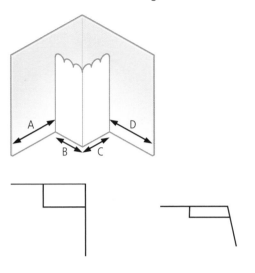

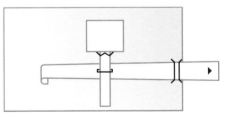

Pivoting motion

There are two different methods of obtaining backwards and forwards motion. Both require a pivot and a connection. It is the relative position of the pivot and the pull-tab that give the precise characteristics of the motion. The following mechanisms tend to work smoothly over a relatively short length of travel. Both types of method can be combined by having two pivot arms on a single pull-tab.

Both methods can be combined

Making a pivoting motion mechanism

Method 1: The pivot arm is attached to the pull-tab above the pivot. This makes the pivot arm move in the same direction as the pull-tab and gives a lot of movement. The pull-tab is secured to the base and has a series of score lines on it, which help it to move easier.

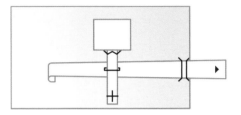

Method 2: The pivot arm is attached to the pull-tab below the pivot, then it moves in the opposite direction to the pull-tab and for a smaller distance. By adjusting the positions of the pivots and length of the pull-tabs, a variety of different movement can be achieved.

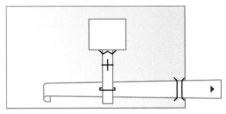

Activities

1 Design a paper mechanism using pivoting motion to advertise a product.

2 Produce a pop-up card using a mechanism of your choice to celebrate an occasion.

Summary

★ All types of paper engineering require careful cutting and gluing.

★ Many types of motion can be achieved using paper engineering.

Systems and control

Exam questions

1 Assess the risks involved in the process of cutting thin board using appropriate tools and equipment. Suggest how the risks can be kept to a minimum. *(5 marks)*

2 Produce a closed loop system diagram for the process of cutting a circle out of thin board using a circle cutter.
(5 marks)

3 Explain why quality is important for:
  a the manufacturer
  b the customer. *(4 marks)*

4 Explain the four main types of motion and give a practical example of each. *(8 marks)*

5 Using a range of annotated sketches, design a pop-up picture to be used in a children's storybook about Halloween. The picture should contain:
  a a suitable mechanism.
  b a feature related to Halloween. *(10 marks)*

6 Social, cultural, moral and environmental issues

This section covers the issues designers and manufacturers need to consider when producing products for a global market.

It is important to apply your understanding of this these issues in your coursework, especially when writing your product specification, so that your design work is informed from the start. Remember that designers and manufacturers are responsible for the effects their products may have on society and the environment. You should consider how your product could be made in the most user-friendly and environmentally-sound way.

What's in this section?

Social, cultural, moral and environmental issues

Social and cultural issues

In this chapter you will:
★ learn about the social and cultural issues related to graphic products
★ learn about the global impact of ICT.

Thinking about graphic products

Designers and manufacturers should consider the end user and make their products acceptable and accessible to as wide a range of customers as possible. This means they must consider the needs of minority groups, including the disabled or elderly.

Packaging

We have all been frustrated by a piece of packaging that seems impossible to open. Imagine the additional difficulties an arthritic or elderly person may experience. Instructions for use and labelling are also areas of concern for people who are partially sighted or have even minor reading difficulties. You can imagine the consequences if safety instructions were misunderstood or simply not read at all. It is important that such instructions are printed in a clear, large font; in a commonly understood language, and that they are displayed in a prominent position on the product so everyone notices them.

Designers and manufacturers create products for people around the world. Therefore, they need to think about all the different places in which the graphic products are sold and how the values and attitudes of each country might influence their design thinking. Clothing, food and the symbolism of certain shapes and colours all play a role in the identity of a particular culture. When a product is intended for use by a range of cultures, it is important to identify and recognise such needs and attitudes so that it will appeal and not be misunderstood or cause offence.

For example, in Hindu cultures the colour red is a symbol of purity, while in most western cultures it can represent sexual passion. Because this colour has opposite meanings in the two cultures, designers must be careful when using red on graphic products. It is important to research a culture before you design a product that might be used there, as colours and images may have a different significance.

Lettering and labelling

Some products, such as chocolate, may be packaged in a variety of ways using things like appropriate lettering styles to reflect the cultural beliefs of the nation. This is so the product appeals to more people. What is attractive in one culture is not necessarily attractive in another.

Products are packaged differently in certain countries to reflect different cultures

Even the name of the product could change. Many Japanese products that are repackaged for sale in Europe have their names altered, partly because a direct translation can mean something entirely different.

The Internet

The Internet is a worldwide network of interconnected computers. Anyone with access to a computer and modem can 'surf' the World Wide Web using a web browser, such as Internet Explorer, and an Internet service provider, such as BT Broadband.

Use of the e-mail and the Internet have revolutionised how we communicate

Websites

In the same way that people are able to find out where we live by using our postal address, each company or individual who sets up an information page on the Internet has their own unique web address beginning with 'www'. As well as being invaluable sources of information, many companies, such as Amazon, use their websites to sell their products and services.

E-mail

One important aspect of the Internet is the ability to communicate information electronically using e-mail. E-mails are delivered almost instantly and you can attach files and documents which might otherwise have to be posted. E-mail has revolutionised the way designers work because there is no longer the need for the designer and the client to live and work closely together. Designers do not even need to be in the same country as their client or manufacturer.

However, disadvantages of e-mail include:

- information can only be sent to people who themselves have access to the Internet
- there is no guarantee the e-mail will be read until the user logs on and checks their inbox
- it is easy to send and receive unwanted mail (known as spam).

Electronic data exchange

As the majority of graphic products are computer generated, files can be sent digitally from the designer to the printing company. This eliminates the time and cost of physically sending designs through the post. Printers use the Internet to set up websites, which act as an 'exchange' for clients. Using this electronic data exchange, printers can receive print files, prepare them for printing and send the proofs back to the designer for checking without having to leave the comfort of their office.

Website design and graphics

The Internet has introduced the whole new idea of website design. All major companies now have a website and graphic designers are employed to create websites that are attractive and interesting to look at. The design of the website depends on what kind of company or product it is: a website design for a pop band will be flashy and fun, but a high-street bank will want a more sophisticated approach that communicates competence and stability.

The design of a website needs to be clear and simple. Just like books, websites must have an index, clear headings and simple-to-follow onscreen instructions.

Coursework

The Internet is a fabulous source of information for your design and technology project. However, examiners will give no credit to students who merely download pages of information and do nothing with it. Make sure any information gained from the Internet is carefully selected and analysed before being included within your design folder.

Activity

1 Explain how the World Wide Web has changed the way graphic designers work.

2 What are the key issues a designer needs to consider when designing a package for use in more than one country?

Summary

★ Designers have a responsibility to produce products that take into account the needs of people from different ethnic groups.

★ ICT has allowed designers greater flexibility in the way a product can be made to meet the needs of a client.

Social, cultural, moral and environmental issues

Moral issues

Moral issues are debates over whether something is right or wrong. The law can make some judgements for us but there are other issues on which we must make up our own mind. For example, some people would argue that it is immoral for banks to loan a low-income family a great deal of money knowing they will struggle to repay it.

Are designers and manufacturers morally responsible if the products they create help to cause problems for this and future generations? A product may have the capacity to exploit, offend, injure or damage the environment around us.

Exploitation

We often take for granted many of the products we use in everyday life. How many of us actually think about where the materials come from, or where and how a product was made?

Developing countries such as those in Africa and South America have been exploited for many years by western corporations, who make vast profits from their raw materials like coffee and abundant, cheap labour. Many workers in these areas of the world are unprotected by employment law and are forced to work long hours for little pay.

Over recent years there has been growing recognition of this problem and more pressure has been put on multi-national companies to recognise the moral obligation they have to their global workforce. The Fair Trade organisation encourages people to buy goods that guarantee a 'fair' percentage of the sale price of a product, such as coffee or chocolate, ends up in the pockets of the indigenous population from the country where the materials are grown, harvested or made.

Planned obsolescence

All products have a lifecycle – they are designed, manufactured and sold. As time goes by, sales of the product start to fall off as new, similar or better products are produced. At this point, manufacturers either revamp the product or cease to produce it. The end of this cycle is called obsolescence (becoming obsolete). The length of the product

Workers in a factory in a developing country

lifecycle varies considerably. It can be anything from a few weeks to several years.

There are three types of obsolescence: natural, technological and planned. **Natural obsolescence** is when a product becomes dated as styles and tastes change over time, or they merely wear out or break. **Technological obsolescence** occurs because new advances in technology lead to new products. For example, digital audio broadcasting (DAB) radios have superseded existing models. **Planned obsolescence** occurs when manufacturers deliberately alter the style of the product to generate sales; products like clothes, mobile phones and cars are constantly being restyled and remarketed. By using planned obsolescence companies safeguard their profits and market dominance. Many argue that this approach breeds a 'throw away' culture where nothing lasts for long and many products are replaced quickly. This in turn leads to more waste and increased pressure on our natural resources to meet the demand for these new products.

Many products are restyled to generate sales

Activities

1 Discuss the issues of exploitation and how companies could balance the need to make profit with the obligation to behave morally towards their global workforce and the environment.

2 Explain what is meant by 'planned obsolescence'.

Summary

★ Designers need to consider the cultural beliefs and values of different societies when designing products.

★ Designers should be aware of the moral issues surrounding the global manufacture of graphic products.

★ Planned obsolescence is used by designers and manufacturers to generate product sales.

Social, cultural, moral and environmental issues

In this chapter you will:
★ learn about how designers and manufacturers deal with the issue of recycling and its effect on the environment.

Designers and manufacturers are responsible for ensuring the products they create will minimise the potential damage to the environment. However, modern society is in conflict with the desire for things new versus the need to protect our environment.

Long life or throw away?

In today's society, many products are regarded as 'throw away' items. The list of such items is long, with small items like toothbrushes to larger items like televisions and fridges. The time when someone would take a household product to be repaired is disappearing. Many everyday products are now being manufactured cheaply due to improved processes and cheap labour that the cost of repair is often more expensive than the cost of buying a new product.

Some of the potential environmental implications of manufacturing graphic products are as follows.

- Card backing, made from wood pulp cut from Canadian forests. The forests have been reduced in size by 60% since 1975. The process of making paper and card uses vast quantities of water and chemicals such as chlorine, which in developing countries may not have such strict waste handling regulations as in Europe. This can lead to extensive water contamination and threaten the populations of these countries.

- Ink, made from pigments derived from plants only found in tropical rainforests. Harvesting these pigments has threatened the existence of the rainforests, which are the planet's natural defence against carbon dioxide emissions.

- Thermoplastic, made from crude oil from the Middle East, Russia and the UK. Oil refineries, drill rigs and oil tankers can cause major pollution if disaster strikes. Also, many political conflicts between countries revolve around oil production. Earth's oil supplies will also eventually run out and we will have to find an alternative raw material for the manufacture of plastic.

Deforestation

How can designers and manufacturers help?

One way of helping to limit the damage to the environment is to use the three Rs approach: reduce, recycle and reuse.

Reduce

Designers and manufacturers can aim to reduce the impact on natural resources and waste production by reducing:
- packaging used to protect a product during transportation and storage
- redundant packaging used to promote a product such as cardboard sleeves on CDs
- the amount of materials being used by making them thinner or by using different shapes requiring less material.

The stapler below is designed to join two sheets of paper together without the use of steel staples. It cuts a hole through the two sheets and then folds over to lock them together. While this is not as strong as a normal stapler, it reduces the amount of materials used by not having steel staples. It is also smaller and does not need so many parts for it to work.

*An environmentally
friendly stapler*

Recycle

Designers should consider whether:

- the product could be made form a recycled material such as paper, glass or aluminium
- it will be easy to recycle the product itself when it has reached the end of its lifespan – this will discourage consumers from dumping the product in a landfill site.

The advantages of recycling are:

- it reduces waste, especially to landfill sites
- it helps to preserve non-renewable resources
- it is becoming more cost effective as local councils provide recycling bins for various uses.

The disadvantages of recycling include:

- there are not enough recycling plants in the UK to encourage regular use
- it is costly because the demand is not great enough yet
- the quality of some products may be reduced compared with new ones made from virgin materials.

Reuse

Designers should try to specify the parts and components that could be reused easily when the product is finished with, such as electronic circuits, fasteners and packaging. They could help to reverse the 'throw away' culture by making products easier and more desirable to repair, perhaps offering cheap upgrades or improvements without having to throw the product away.

Some manufacturers are now providing consumers with products in containers that can be reused or refilled. For example, washing liquid capsules are available in plastic containers. These containers can be refilled with capsules from a bag, using less material and producing less waste.

Activities

1 Give three advantages of recycling.

2 Write a list of everything you recycle and share the results with the rest of your class.

Summary

★ Designers and manufacturers are responsible for ensuring the products they make will minimise the potential damage to the environment.

★ Designers and manufacturers can help to minimise the effects on the environment by using the three Rs approach: reduce, recycle and reuse.

Social, cultural, moral and environmental issues

6.4 Environmental issues 2: The packaging issue

> **In this chapter you will:**
> ★ learn about why products are packaged
> ★ learn about the environmental issues related to packaging.

Why is packaging used?

There are five main reasons why products are packaged:
- Protection: products need to be protected during transport and storage to ensure they reach the consumer in perfect condition.
- Preservation: food products need to be kept fresh for use and kept from contamination.
- Promotion: eye-catching packaging, which attracts consumers to buy the product and helps them recognise a brand, is important when selling a product.
- Containment: products that are loose, like sweets, flour and drinks, need to be contained.
- Information: it is important to tell consumers what the product is and to inform them about health and safety and environmental issues.

Increases in packaging

In recent years, there has been an increase in the amount of packaging used for a whole range of products. The main reasons are:
- customers prefer to see products with high-quality packaging as it gives the impression that what they are buying is good quality
- legislation now requires that products have improved labelling to inform consumers about the contents and any health and safety issues
- there is a greater need for tamper-proof designs – this is to stop products being damaged or altered in any way, such as food contamination
- to help sell more products, for example multi-pack offers
- to make transport and storage of products easier – blister packs are used for small products like batteries, stationary and computer hardware.

Disposal of packaging

The major problem associated with packaging is disposal. Ninety per cent of packaging is thrown away and ends up in landfill sites. Because most of this packaging is not biodegradable, waste material from packaging has increased tenfold since the 1960s with every household creating, on average, three large bin bags of rubbish each week.

Packaging labels

Labels on packaging can be categorised into the following areas:
- Legal requirements such as ingredients, weights, nutritional information, safety issues and 'sell by' dates on food packaging.

Gentle pH-balanced formula is suitable for everyday use.
* Apply to scalp and hair, ensuring full coverage from root to tip. Gently massage in. Rinse, and repeat if desired. For best results, use every time you shampoo your hair.

Avoid contact with eyes. If contact occurs, rinse thoroughly with water.

ingredients
Aqua, Ammonium Laureth Sulfate, Ammonium Lauryl Sulfate, Sodium Chloride, Glycol Distearate, Dimethicone, Zinc Pyrithione, Citric Acid, Cetyl Alcohol, Sodium Citrate, Ammonium Xylenesulfonate, Cocamide MEA, Guar Hydroxypropyltrimonium Chloride, Parfum, Hydrogenated Polydecene, Sodium Benzoate, Butylphenyl Methylpropional, Trimethylolpropane Tricaprylate/Tricaprate, DMDM Hydantoin, Tetrasodium EDTA, Linalool, Benzyl Salicylate, Hexyl Cinnamal, Benzyl Alcohol, Limonene, Geraniol, Sodium Polynaphthalenesulfonate, Paraffinum Liquidum, Methylchloroisothiazolinone, CI 60730, CI 42090, Methylisothiazolinone, Tocopherol.

Procter & Gamble UK, Weybridge, Surrey, KT13 0XP, UK Made in EU
(GB) Comments? ☎ 0800 7312892 (IRL) Comments? ☎ 1800 409066
(RSA) Comments? ☎ 0800 001959

12M

5 000174 900637 >

400 ml ℮

A shampoo bottle label

- Recycling information.

This symbol means the item can be recycled

- Bar codes for identification and quality control.

A barcode

Activity

a Investigate a small range of packaging: sweet wrappers, chocolate boxes, gift wraps, etc. Analyse each one to see how each of the five main reasons why products are packaged is applied to each example.

Summary

★ There are five main reasons for packaging a product.

★ Product packaging has increased for a number of reasons.

★ Packaging leads to increased waste in landfill sites.

- Other information such as suitability for vegetarians and customer service phone numbers.

cauldron

Why not try this? Serve with roasted garlic cloves and red onion slices, with crispy golden sweet potato wedges and a spicy mayonnaise dip.

Easy to cook: Remove all packaging, then;
Fry: Lightly fry for 6-8 minutes in a small amount of oil in a non-stick pan over a medium heat, turning frequently.
Grill: Place under a hot grill for 6-8 minutes, turning frequently. (All appliances vary, these are guidelines only).

Ingredients: Tofu (39%) (Water, Soya Beans), Onions (17%), Water, Vegetable Fat (Vegetable Fat, Wheat Flour), Wholemeal Rusk (Wheat Flour, Water, Salt, Raising Agents: Ammonium Carbonates), Free Range Egg Albumen, Yeast, Stabiliser: Methyl Cellulose, Hydrolysed Vegetable Protein (Vegetable Protein, Soya Oil), Tapioca Starch, Yeast Extract (Yeast, Salt), Salt, Sausage Seasoning (Wheat Flour, Spice, Herbs, Vegetable Oil, Spice Extracts, Herb Extracts), Fructose, Sage, Roasted Barley Malt Extract, Pepper Extract.

✔ **Contains: Barley & Wheat Gluten, Egg and Soya.**

Made with Non GM ingredients.
Not suitable for people with a nut allergy.
Recycled Board

Cauldron is about food that's imaginative and easy to prepare. We like the fresh ideas that come from blending contemporary cooking with a broad range of cultural influences. Wherever we can, we choose simply-prepared, natural ingredients, because a meal is only as good as what we put into it.

Enjoy this at its best:
From the fridge: Can be kept unopened until the Use By date at 4°C in the refrigerator. Once opened consume within 48 hours.
From the Freezer: Freeze on day of purchase for up to 1 month in a 4-star deep freeze. Do not refreeze once thawed.
(From frozen, defrost thoroughly and follow chilled cooking instructions).

Nutrition information

Typical Values as sold	Per 100g	Per sausage (50g)
Energy	767kJ	383kJ
	185kcal	92kcal
Protein	9.3g	4.6g
Carbohydrate	3.5g	1.7g
of which sugars	2.4g	1.2g
Fat	16.1g	8.0g
of which saturates	8.8g	4.4g
Dietary fibre	2.8g	1.4g
Sodium	1.0g	0.5g
Salt	2.5g	1.2g

Want to contact us? Cauldron Foods Ltd, Portishead, Bristol, BS20 7BF
www.cauldronfoods.co.uk Telephone:01275 818448

5 succulent Lincolnshire **veggie sausages**

From the Freezer: Freeze on day of purchase for up to 1 month in a 4-star deep freeze. Do not refreeze once thawed.
(From frozen, defrost thoroughly and follow chilled cooking instructions).

Nutrition information

Typical Values as sold	Per 100g	Per sausage (50g)
Energy	767kJ	383kJ
	185kcal	92kcal
Protein	9.3g	4.6g
Carbohydrate	3.5g	1.7g
of which sugars	2.4g	1.2g
Fat	16.1g	8.0g
of which saturates	8.8g	4.4g
Dietary fibre	2.8g	1.4g
Sodium	1.0g	0.5g
Salt	2.5g	1.2g

5 013683 100825

250g ℮

Want to contact us? Cauldron Foods Ltd, Portishead, Bristol, BS20 7BF
www.cauldronfoods.co.uk Telephone:01275 818448

Packaging labels contain other relevant information

Social, cultural, moral and environmental issues

Exam questions

1 Explain how cultural differences of many countries might affect the design of a graphic product. *(2 marks)*

2 Give two advantages for using recycled card in a graphic product. *(4 marks)*

3 Give a reason why recycled card is not used for packaging food products. *(2 marks)*

4 Design a symbol to be displayed on a piece of packaging to inform the consumer that the materials used contain 50% recycled material. *(6 marks)*

7

Industrial practices

This section covers all the industrial processes involved in printing and producing graphic products. You need to understand these processes so that you can show how the products you design could be made commercially.

What's in this section?

7.1 An introduction to industrial practices

In this chapter you will:

★ learn a wide range of industrial terms and terminology

★ learn how a graphic product is produced industrially.

A range of industrially produced graphic products

In order to make informed decisions about the graphic products you are designing, it is important to understand how products we use in everyday life are produced. The processes followed by printers, print finishers and die cutters are collectively called industrial practices. Each of these industrial processes affects the product in some way and gives different qualities and features. The choice of industrial process is usually determined by the desired function (what you need the graphic product to do), the cost, the aesthetics (how you want the product to look) and the quantity required.

Look carefully at the front cover of the book above and you will begin to consider the range and extent of industrial processes used. Think carefully about the reasons that led the designer to use the chosen processes.

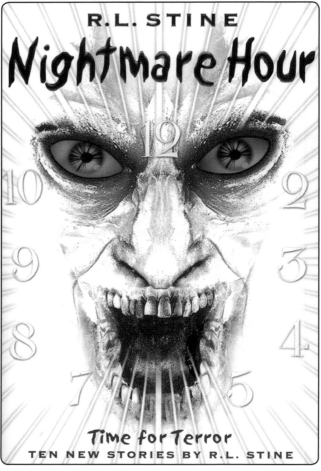

A book cover incorporating a range of industrial print and print-finishing processes

The cover has been printed using a four-colour, high-speed process. Metal-coated plastic films with holographic images have been pressed (blocked) onto the eyes. The title lettering has been embossed. The book cover has been laminated to protect it and to make it more rigid. Finally, the raised lettering has been spot varnished to make it really stand out. In addition, all the press signatures (pages) have been folded, collated (placed in the correct order), stitched (bound) and trimmed to the required size using a guillotine.

All graphic products start life as a working drawing. Before computers were used, this working drawing was called 'camera ready copy'. Today, designers produce their drawings using sophisticated design software. The process of producing the working drawing is called origination.

When originating the working drawing, the designer has to ensure that it is produced exactly as required. In order to do this, he or she needs to think carefully about the design and layout. For example, a bleed area needs to be built in. Bleed occurs because the paper absorbs the wet inks, even though very fast drying inks are used now. Usually 2–4 mm are added to the edge of a page. Background colours always go over the edge of the page to ensure that, when trimmed, the colour goes right to the edge. There is also a tolerance built in for creasing and cropping. A tolerance is the amount by which a cut or fold varies from its intended position. For example, a trimmed edge may be +/– 0.5 mm from the intended position – this means that the edge may vary by up to 1 mm in total. Designers need to allow for this. Therefore, margins and spaces are always incorporated into working drawings.

When sent to the printer, the working drawing is accompanied by a manufacturing specification. This specification lists the typefaces (fonts) used, the code numbers of the colours required and other technical details. Using the working drawing and specification, the printer is able to set the images ready for print production.

Coursework

It is an essential requirement of the coursework that all products are designed to be made in quantity using industrial processes.

Activities

1 Collect a range of textbooks and look carefully at the covers of each. Using the headings 'function' and 'aesthetics', list the different processes used, giving reasons for each.

2 Use the Internet to investigate how plastic carrier bags are printed.

Summary

★ The choice of industrial process is usually determined by the function, cost, aesthetics and the quantity required.

★ The process of developing the working drawing is known as origination.

A proof copy of a leaflet with printers' marks applied

A good way of understanding the industrial production of graphic products is to consider it as a control process with an input, a process and an output. Some of the main operations are shown in the diagram below.

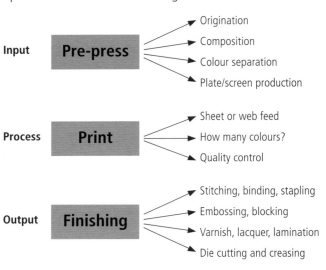

Input — Pre-press
- Origination
- Composition
- Colour separation
- Plate/screen production

Process — Print
- Sheet or web feed
- How many colours?
- Quality control

Output — Finishing
- Stitching, binding, stapling
- Embossing, blocking
- Varnish, lacquer, lamination
- Die cutting and creasing

Main pre-press operations

The word pre-press is used to describe the processes carried out in preparation for the printing, or pressing, of graphic products. The main pre-press operations are:

- colour separation
- production of film negatives
- addition of printers' marks
- plate or screen production.

In industrial printing companies, a skilled person known as an image setter carries out the pre-press operations.

From artwork to print

Before an illustration or design can be printed, a printing plate must be made. The plate is usually made from an aluminium sheet and contains the negative (back to front) photographic image of the picture that needs to be printed.

Unlike text, all pictures or illustrations are either line drawings or tone illustrations. A line drawing could be a black and white drawing, graph or chart, whereas a tone illustration is like a photograph and is made up of shades rather than definite lines. Each type of illustration needs different treatment.

Line drawings

The photographic image used to make a plate is produced using a process camera. A process camera is a large piece of photographic equipment that can have special lenses and filters attached to it. Producing a negative image of a line drawing using a process camera is a straightforward process. On a negative line drawing image, all the black lines of the subject appear as transparent lines and the white background appears as black.

A negative image

Tone illustrations

Tone illustrations need to be broken up into a series of dots before they can be printed. The dark parts of the picture are made from large dots and the light areas from small dots. From a distance, the human eye cannot see these dots individually. Look at the photograph below. It has clear areas of light and dark tones.

Photos are tone illustrations

If you look at an image in a magazine or newspaper through a magnifying glass, you can easily see the different-sized dots.

The dots that make up the image

The screen size used for newsprint produces a poorer-quality image

This image has a much higher definition than newsprint because it is has a larger screen size

To make this pattern of dots, the original photograph is scanned through a screen. A screen is a piece of film that is covered in thousands of tiny dots like a fine mesh. It has the effect of creating dots on the negative.

The density of the screen (the number of dots in a line) affects how sharp the final picture is. The higher the screen size, the better the quality. Compare the quality of a newspaper picture (screen size 80 dots) with a picture in a magazine (screen size 150–300 dots). Remember, however, that another reason why the screen size on newspapers is so low is that the paper used is very absorbent, causing the ink to bleed when printed.

Activity

Collect a series of pictures from different publications such as newspapers and magazines. Using a powerful magnifying glass or digital microscope, look at each picture in turn to determine how screen size affects the quality of the image.

Summary

★ The image setter takes the original images from the designer and prepares them for printing.

★ The word pre-press is used to describe the processes carried out in preparation for printing.

★ Tone illustrations need to be broken up into a series of dots before they can be printed.

Industrial practices

A full-colour image is built up as each colour is printed on top of the previous colour

In this chapter you will:

★   **learn the correct names and purposes of the four process colours**

★   **understand why the four process colours need to be separated out from a full-colour image as part of the pre-press stage of production.**

If you look at a magazine with coloured pictures, you will see a mixture of many colours. At first glance it appears that thousands of different coloured inks have been used. In fact, all the different colours are usually produced from just four colours. These four colours are cyan (blue), magenta (red), yellow and black. These four colours are known in printing technology as the process colours and are referred to as **CMYK** for short. They represent the three primary colours together with black and, from these colours, all other colours can be produced. The letter K used for black stands for 'key' because it is the key that brings the image to life.

Colour fusion

When viewed under a powerful magnifying glass or microscope, you can see clearly that the image below is made up of a series of dots. Because the dots are small and close together, the human eye blends or 'fuses' them into a solid colour.

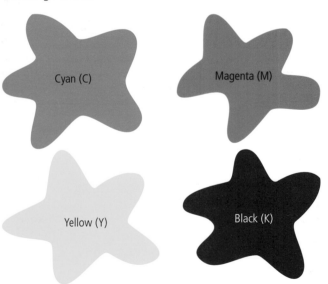
The process colours

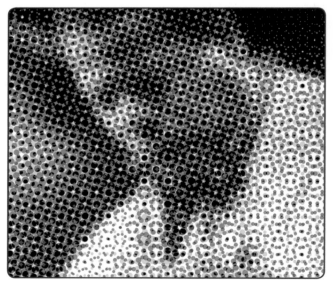
Colour fusion in action – when viewed under a magnifying glass, the dots can be seen clearly

In order to produce a full-colour print, these four colours are printed separately one after the other. In this way, the eye sees all the colours in various amounts and is deceived into thinking that the whole range of colour is present. The order that the four colours are printed changes according to the nature of the graphic being printed.

To achieve this full-colour effect, four different printing plates of the same subject are needed: one to print cyan, one for magenta, one for yellow and one for black. When making these plates, the printer uses a process called colour separation.

Colour separation

To produce a colour separation of the image, a process camera or scanner is used. The process camera uses a special glass filter that only allows one colour through. The image setter takes four pictures of the same subject using a different coloured filter each time. The most common method of colour separation is to use a special scanner that has built-in colour filters. This method is less time-consuming for the image setter. The image is produced through a screen so that each colour is broken up into a series of dots. The scanner produces four separate pieces of film. These in turn are used to make the four printing plates.

Mixing primary colours together makes a new or secondary colour. For example, mixing together blue (cyan) and yellow makes green. In order to print a full-colour image, the printer has to work in reverse to this by separating out the process colours from the original.

The original image made up from the four process colours CMYK

The image setter scans the original file using special colour filters. A colour filter blocks certain colours and only allows the colour you want through. For example, if you hold a piece of blue glass or plastic up to your eyes, the image you see will be blue because only blue light can pass through. The colour filters used by the image setter enable a separate film to be made of the subject in each of the four process colours.

The scanner produces four separate pieces of film, one for each of the four process colours – these are then used to produce the printing plates or screens

✎ Activities

1 Name the four process colours.

2 Which two process colours are mixed to make the secondary colour purple?

3 What is meant by the term 'colour separation'?

Summary

★ The four process colours are cyan, magenta, yellow and black. They are called CMYK for short.

★ In order to produce a full-colour print, each of the four process colours has to be separated and printed individually.

Industrial practices

Printers' marks and quality control

In this chapter you will:

★ **learn about the different printers' marks and why they are used**

★ **learn about the importance of quality control in the production of graphic products.**

When a large number of graphic products are being made, it is important that the standard of quality is the same for each one. The customer expects to get good value for money from a quality product. The manufacturer needs to make the products as efficiently as possible with little or no waste. In order to achieve a consistent quality, the manufacturer uses quality control and quality assurance techniques.

Quality control is used to check that the products produced meet the required quality standard. This means making a series of checks for things like colour and size. Graphic products that are printed use a series of printers' marks for quality control. The image setter adds printers' marks during the pre-press stage. The main printers' marks are:

- registration marks
- colour bars
- crop marks.

Registration marks

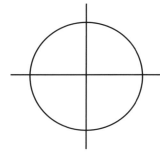

A registration mark

Registration marks, or targets, are used to accurately align the printing plates on top of each other. They are usually placed at the top, bottom, left and right of the page. Registration marks are important because if printing plates are not aligned correctly, the printed image will appear fuzzy or 'out of register'.

The printer checks the registration marks using a magnifying glass to make sure the plates are accurately aligned.

Cyan and magenta registration marks viewed under a magnifying glass are seen to be out of register

Colour bars

Colour bars, or **densitometer** scales as they are often called, are used by printers to check the quality of colour during printing. One colour bar is produced for each printing ink used. As you can see from the magenta colour bar below, it is a scale giving different tones or densities of colour. On the scale, 100% represents solid colour, 50% half-tone, etc.

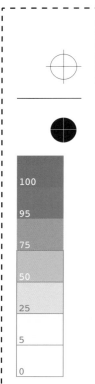

Colour profile: Disabled Composite

Colour bars are used for checking the density of colour during the print run

During printing, the printer uses a hand-held device called a densitometer to measure the density of colour. The reading from the densitometer will show whether or not the colour is being printed consistently. Any adjustments or colour corrections can be made at this point.

Crop marks

Crop marks are located on each of the four corners of the page. They mark the outline edge of the page and provide a guide for the guillotine blade when trimming the paper to size.

A printer's copy of a leaflet showing crop marks

On most graphic products, the printers' marks are trimmed off by the guillotine as part of the finishing process. However, on some products such as a newspapers or cereal cartons, the printer's marks can be seen.

Activities

1 What are the three main printers' marks and how are they used?

2 What is meant by the term 'out of register'?

3 What is a densitometer?

4 This activity involves comparing the printers' marks and print quality on a newspaper and a packaging carton.
   a Collect a breakfast cereal carton and a double-page spread from a newspaper.
   b Carefully take apart the breakfast cereal packaging. Look at the printers' marks that remain – these may well be on the gluing tab. Identify any printers' marks that have been used.
   c Study the newspaper spread and identify any printers' marks that have been used.
   d Using a magnifying glass, compare the accuracy of the registration on each product.
   e Make a list of the marks used with specific reference to colours, crop and registration marks.

Summary

★ Printers' marks are added to the print file to enable the printer to carry out quality control tests during printing.

★ The guillotine often trims off printers' marks when the graphic product is finished to size.

Industrial practices

Offset lithography

7.5

In this chapter you will:

★ **learn how to produce printing plates from film images.**

Offset **lithography** is the most common form of commercial printing. It accounts for more than 70% of all printed materials. From magazines to leaflets and product packaging, offset lithography has been the most popular choice for manufacturers because of the print quality it achieves.

Basic principles

Offset lithography works on a simple principle: ink and water do not mix. Images (words and art) are put on plates, which are dampened, first by water and then ink. The ink sticks to the image area, the water to the non-image area. Then the image is transferred to a rubber blanket, and from the rubber blanket to paper. That is why the process is called 'offset' – the image does not go directly to the paper from the plates, as it does in many other forms of printing.

The main stages of the process are as follows.

1 Original artwork – photographs, illustrations and text – are scanned and entered into a computer.

2 These elements are combined into a document using page makeup software.

3 Full-size films are output using a high-resolution image setter. These could be either positives or negatives.

4 Printing plates are made from the films using a photochemical process. The plates are exposed to high-intensity light through the films and then chemically treated so that non-image areas are water absorbent.

5 The flexible plates are attached to the plate cylinders of a litho press and the job is printed.

From image to plate

Before each of the four-colour plates is produced, a film image must be set for each separated colour. Full-size clear plastic films are produced using a machine similar to a printer called an image setter. These films are similar to transparencies used on overhead projectors.

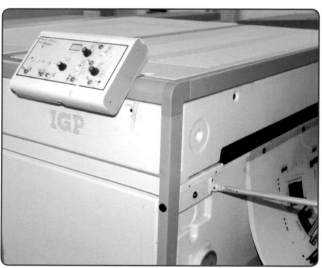

An image setter is used to produce the clear film images needed to make the printing plates

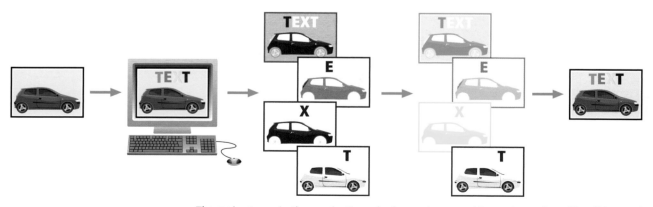

The main stages in the production of a four-colour graphic product using offset lithography

The film images produced on the image setter could be either positives or negatives. The picture below shows a film image produced for a magenta colour separation.

Magenta separation

Plate production

Images from the film are transferred to printing plates in much the same way as photographs are developed. A measured amount of light is allowed to pass through the film to expose the printing plate. When the plates are exposed to light, a chemical reaction occurs that allows

an ink-receptive coating to be activated. This results in the transfer of the image from the film to the plate. The process is widely known as photomechanical transfer (PMT).

The material used for the printing plates is aluminium. This is used because:

- it is flexible
- it is durable so has long life – particularly important on long print runs
- it is cost effective.

Once produced, the plates are checked for accuracy before production begins.

Once all four plates have been produced and undergone quality control checks, print production is now ready to start. Occasionally five or six colours are used to achieve high-quality, full-colour images.

Coursework

It is likely that you will include details of offset lithography as part of your research into materials and processes.

Activities

1   List the five main stages in the offset lithographic process.

2   Explain what 'offset' means in the process offset lithography.

Summary

★   A separate clear plastic film is produced for each printing plate.

★   Printing plates are made from aluminium because it is low cost, flexible and durable.

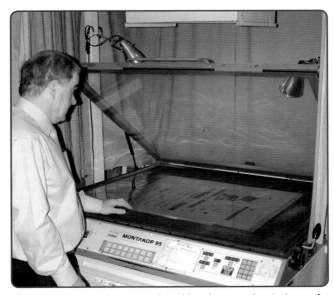

A printing plate being produced by photomechanical transfer

In this chapter you will:

★   learn the difference between sheet-fed and web-fed lithography.

You have already learned that the underlying principle of the lithographic process is that ink and water do not mix. Look carefully at the diagram below to see how the image is transferred from the plate to the paper.

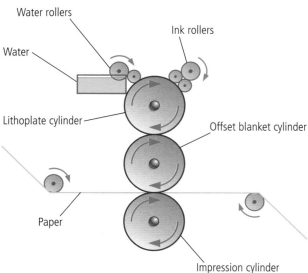

Water rollers

Ink rollers

Water

Lithoplate cylinder

Offset blanket cylinder

Paper

Impression cylinder

The offset lithography process

Once produced, the printing plates are attached to a lithoplate cylinder. The ink is distributed to the plates through a series of rollers. On the press, the plates are dampened, first by water rollers and then ink rollers. The rollers distribute the ink from the ink fountain onto the plates.

The image areas of the plate pick up ink from the ink rollers. The water rollers keep the ink off the non-image areas of the plate. Each plate then transfers its image to a rubber blanket cylinder, which in turn transfers the image to the paper. The plate itself does not actually touch the paper – thus the term 'offset' lithography. All of this occurs at an extremely high speed.

Offset lithography printing presses vary in size and complexity. They range from very small two-colour presses through to large six-colour presses with the capability of producing 60,000 prints (presses) per hour.

An offset lithography press with a printing plate attached

Sheet-fed and web-fed presses

The press can be fed either with paper one sheet at a time (sheet fed) or from a large roll of paper (web fed). Web printing is normally reserved for large-scale, long-run work such as magazines and catalogues.

Sheet-fed offset lithography

Sheet feeders are common and are used extensively by small to medium-sized print companies on small presses. Sheet feeding devices use pneumatic (air-controlled) suckers to lift one sheet of paper at a time and feed it into the press. Therefore, sheet-fed presses have relatively slow rates of production.

A four-colour sheet-fed lithography press

Web-fed offset lithography

With web-fed printing, the paper or card is fed through the press as one continuous stream pulled from rolls of paper. Each roll can weigh as much as one tonne. The paper is cut to size after printing.

Web presses print at very high speeds and use large sheets of paper. Press speeds can reach up to 60,000 impressions per hour.

Large web-fed presses allow speeds of up to 60,000 presses per hour to be achieved

Even when a one-tonne roll of paper runs out, the presses do not stop rolling. The new roll can be joined to the old one as the web press is running. At the moment the join occurs, the rolls of paper stop rotating for a split second, at which point the paper is taped together automatically. Large offset web presses are fast, economical and produce high-quality print.

The advantages and disadvantages of offset lithography are explained in the table below.

Activity

In pairs, make a list of graphic products that could be produced by web-fed offset lithography.

Summary

★ Sheet-fed presses are used on small presses.

★ Sheet-fed presses lift one sheet of paper at a time and feed it into the press.

★ Web-fed presses print at very high speeds and use large sheets of paper.

★ Web-fed presses can print up to 60,000 impressions per hour.

Advantages	Disadvantages
Prints four or more colours on a range of flat materials	Less economical than rotogravure and flexography on high-volume printing of 1 million +
A high-quality process	Less economical than digital printing on small to medium runs of 50–5,000, although quality is slightly higher – especially true of web-fed presses
A very economical process on medium to large-scale production runs of 500–500,000	Limited to the materials it can print on to – much less flexible than other forms of printing such as screen printing
A fast process – speeds of up to 60,000 prints per hour can be achieved	

The advantages and disadvantages of offset lithography

Industrial practices

Screen process printing

> **In this chapter you will:**
> ★ **learn how screen process printing works.**

Screen printing uses a stencil through which the ink is pushed. The process involves forcing ink through a fine mesh (screen), which helps to spread the ink evenly. It is a popular and well-used process because it can print onto virtually any surface from glass to wood.

The screen process

To begin, a film positive (clear or velum) is printed using a printer. A laser printer is best, but inkjet printers will work too. As with all industrial printing processes, to ensure consistent quality when manufacturing in quantity a registration mark must be added (see page 112).

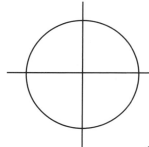

A registration mark

In order to print two or more colours a separate film positive is needed for each colour.

The next step is to prepare a screen. This is polyester mesh that is stretched tightly and glued to either a wooden or a metal frame. The mesh that is used comes in different sizes. For example, a 110 mesh count means it has 110 holes per square inch and a 300 mesh count has 300 holes per square inch. The more holes in the screen, the finer the detail your print will be; the fewer holes, the more course the print will be.

The next stage is to coat the screen with photosensitive emulsion. This is spread evenly onto both sides of the screen. The emulsion is sensitive to ultraviolet rays, so it is essential not to have sunlight, fluorescent light or halogen light in the room. The screen is then left for about 45 minutes in a dark area to dry.

Once the screen has dried, it can have the image photographically 'burned' onto it. The film positive is placed over the underside of the screen using the registration marks for alignment. It is placed on the back of the screen so that when you print the image it will be the correct way round.

A piece of heavy glass is laid over the positive. This is to ensure that the edges are crisp and clear and that the image washes out easily.

The glass is placed on the image

A halogen light is turned on for five minutes. It is important that there is no ultraviolet light in the same room, or any other screens that have emulsion on that are not ready to be exposed. Next, the image is washed out, which takes about five minutes. As the water runs over the image, it gradually starts falling through where the image is (the image looks white). It is important that washing out is not done in the sunlight or under any ultraviolet light. Only when the image is clearly washed can it be brought out into daylight. The screen is then taped to the inside of the frame ready for production.

The screen is washed out

Producing the screen print

The lightest colour of ink is placed down first. The tool with a rubber blade in the photo below is called a squeegee. Squeegees come in different lengths and must be a little wider than the image being printed.

The correct procedure is to push the ink with the squeegee from the back of the screen towards the operator, coating the screen with a thick layer of ink. Next, pushing down hard, the ink is forced through one time only from front to back.

Using the squeegee to apply ink to the screen image

Advantages of screen printing

Screen process printing is a widely used commercial process. It is popular because:

- it is easy to use
- it is versatile and can print onto virtually all materials
- it requires low initial capital investment
- it is a relatively low-cost process for short to medium print runs
- when automated screen printing presses are used, speeds of up to 6,000 impressions per hour can be achieved.

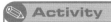

Activity

In pairs, make a list of graphic products that could be produced using screen process printing.

Summary

★ Screen process printing uses a stencil through which the ink is pushed.

★ It is a popular and well-used process because it can print onto virtually any surface.

Industrial practices

Relief printing

Letterpress

Letterpress, also known as relief printing, is the oldest form of printing. The process is one of the easiest to understand. Letterpress printing starts with a single piece or multiple pieces of metal (or wood) made up of an image or letters of type on a printing plate. The area that is intended to be printed is raised up higher than other areas of the plate. Ink is applied by rollers to the raised surfaces. The raised surfaces then press on paper and the ink, from the raised areas, is left on the paper. The print quality can be sharp and clear, but it can vary depending on the quality and texture of the paper. Letterpress printing is rare today and not considered to be a commercial production process.

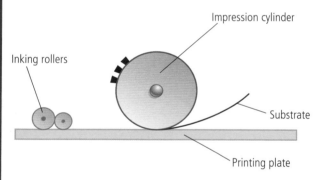

The raised surface on the impression cylinder is inked and prints directly onto the surface

The first letterpress printing plate was created by making a plaster mould of a type form and then casting a metal duplicate of the original, called a stereotype. Stereotyping became an extremely important technology during the Industrial Revolution because it yielded a one-piece printing surface that could be used in place of the original type form on a variety of automated printing presses. Curved stereotypes cast from papier mâché moulds were used on rotary letterpresses for printing daily newspapers until the early 1970s, when typesetting equipment changed radically and hot-metal machine typesetting was largely replaced by computer typesetting.

Flexography

Flexography, also known as aniline printing, is a widely used commercial printing process for producing a wide range of graphic products that are needed in very large amounts, usually in excess of 500,000. Frequently used for printing on plastic, foil, acetate film, brown paper, newsprint and other materials used in packaging, flexography uses flexible printing plates made of soft rubber or plastic. The inked plates with a slightly raised image are rotated on a cylinder, which transfers the image to the surface.

Flexography uses fast-drying inks, is a high-speed print process, can print on many types of absorbent and non-absorbent materials, and can print repeat patterns such as for gift wrap and wallpaper. It is a high-speed process, typically producing up to 60,000 presses per hour.

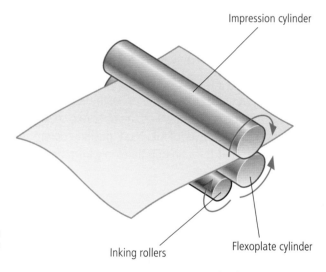

The flexography process

The key principles of the flexography process are as follows.
- Each colour is ready mixed and can be applied in large, solid areas.
- It is limited to combinations of single colours (usually no more than three).
- It is economical for between 250 and 5,000 copies using hand-fed machinery.
- It is economical for very high volumes (250,000 to 10 million) using fully automated machinery.
- A limited quality can be achieved.

Flexography is a popular choice for printing onto plastic film used in product packaging

Activity

Relief printing such as flexography and letterpress produces blocks of solid colours, as opposed to lithography and screen process printing, which produce a series of dots. Using a powerful magnifying glass or digital microscope, identify three products that have been printed using flexography.

Summary

★ Letterpress is based on inking a raised surface and pressing it directly against the material to be printed.

★ Letterpress is rare today and is not considered to be a commercial production process.

★ Flexography uses flexible printing plates made of rubber or plastic and is frequently used for plastic, foil, acetate film, brown paper and other materials used in packaging.

★ Flexography uses fast-drying inks, is a high-speed print process, can print on many types of absorbent and non-absorbent materials, and can print repeat patterns.

Industrial practices

Print finishing and varnishing

Print finishing

Print finishing is used to create a whole range of different effects that will help to sell and protect the graphic product. For example, most book covers need to be protected in some way in order to ensure they look good for a long time and do not become dirty when handled. Varnishing a wooden product after manufacture stops dirty fingerprints spoiling its appearance (protection) and makes it look good (aesthetics). This is exactly the same for paper and board. Quick-drying varnishes are used so that graphic products which are handled regularly do not deteriorate quickly.

GCSE Design & Technology for **AQA**

Graphic Products

Geoff Hancock • Keith Bolling

Series editor: Geoff Hancock

Heinemann

Inspiring generations

Book covers need to have a protective surface finish to stop them becoming dirty when handled

Print finishes therefore have two basic functions: to protect the product and to make it more aesthetically pleasing. However, the main factor that must be considered by a manufacturer before taking the decision to use a particular print finish is the additional cost. Print finishing usually requires a separate process, which can be expensive and adds to the final cost of the product. Also, print finishing often uses specialist techniques and is not usually carried out by the printers themselves.

The main finishes applied to printed products are:
- varnishing
- laminating
- embossing
- foil blocking.

These finishes are often used in combination in order to achieve particular effects.

Varnishing

Varnishing is the most common finishing process used on graphic products. Sometimes it is applied to the whole surface and sometimes it is applied to specific areas (spot varnishing). Varnishes that are applied to the whole surface are often referred to as roller coat or book varnish. Roller coat varnish is often applied directly to printed sheets using one of the printing stations on an offset lithography printer.

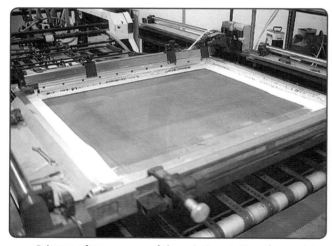

Printers often use one of the printing stations for applying varnish

One of the most common types of varnish is called ultraviolet (UV) varnish. UV varnish dries when it is passed under an ultraviolet light source. UV varnish requires two additional units on a printing press: a UV light unit and a refrigeration unit.

The UV unit gets very hot during use and there is a danger that the original inks may reactivate and damage the print quality. For this reason, a refrigeration unit is needed to cool down the paper after it has passed through the UV light box.

Spot varnishing is a high-gloss UV varnish that is applied to a selected area of the printed image. It is carried out to enhance product impact or to form part of the graphic design. The process of screen printing is used to apply spot varnish. Spot varnishing is a more expensive process than standard UV varnishing because of the additional work required. However, using spot varnish with special effects such as glitter can help to create very exciting graphic effects.

Glitter varnish with spot varnish on top

 Activities

1. Why might a designer decide to use UV varnish on a graphic product?

2. What is the difference between roller coat and spot varnish?

3. In pairs, make a list of graphic products that could be finished using varnish.

 Summary

★ Print finishing is widely used to create a range of different effects that will help to sell and protect the graphic product.

★ Print finishes have two basic functions: to protect the product and to make it more aesthetically pleasing.

Industrial practices

Laminating, embossing and foil blocking

In this chapter you will:

★ learn the key principles of laminating, embossing and foil blocking.

Laminating

Varnishing is a relatively low-cost solution for protecting a printed surface but it does not produce a waterproof seal. Designers or manufacturers sometimes require a high degree of protection. In this case, lamination is used. The most common commercial lamination process uses a water-based adhesive similar to PVA glue to fix thin polyester or polypropylene film to the surface of the paper or card.

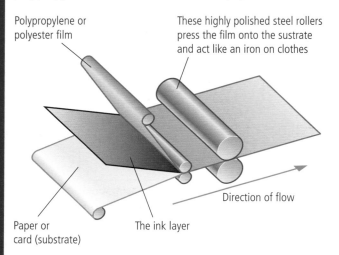

Polypropylene or polyester film

These highly polished steel rollers press the film onto the sustrate and act like an iron on clothes

Direction of flow

Paper or card (substrate)

The ink layer

The basic process of lamination

As with all print finishes, lamination is used both as a protector and as a basis for improving the aesthetics of a product. Unlike varnishing, lamination improves the strength and the protective qualities of the product. In essence, lamination provides:

• water proofing
• chemical and heat resistance
• physical strength
• improved visual qualities.

The thin plastic film that is applied is known as a laminate. Laminates vary in thickness but they are usually between 8 and 15 microns. A micron is 1/1000th of a millimetre. Therefore, 8 microns is 0.008 mm thick. Even though laminates are very thin, they significantly stiffen the paper

and board, which is why they are often used for book covers. The process of lamination is often combined with other finishing processes such as spot varnishing in order to create interesting graphic effects. Look carefully at the photo below. This material started out as a high-gloss card. The material was then laminated with a 15 micron matt laminate, which makes the background dull. The title was then spot varnished onto the matt laminate. The effect that has been created is that the title really stands out against the matt background.

A full-gloss board is matt laminated and then spot varnished to create a sophisticated visual effect

Embossing

Embossing is a common process used to create an interesting effect on the surface of the material. In its simplest form, embossing involves creating a textured roller

Embossing creates a raised (or indented) surface onto a wide range of materials

or stamp and using force to impress the image into the surface of the material. Embossing creates a raised surface on the work.

Embossing presses can be hand-operated or automatic. Automatic presses use up to five tonnes of pressure to create the embossed effect.

Texturising paper and board

Graphic products such as book covers are often given a texture to increase their stiffness and to make them visually more interesting. These textures are usually applied to laminated surfaces.

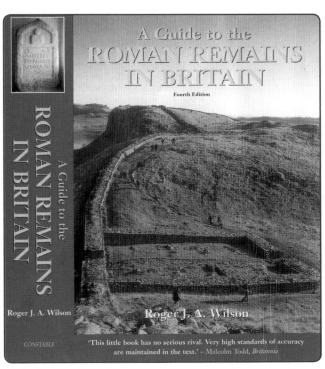

A plain laminated sheet is passed between textured rollers in order to give the final product a textured surface

Embossing rollers are used by commercial finishers to apply grain effects to paper, board and varnished laminates. A pair of rollers (like on an old-fashioned mangle) impress their texture onto the material. The rollers are about 1.5 metres wide and a pair costs in the region of £5,000 to £10,000.

A good way of creating the effect of embossing is to use an ICT program such as Adobe Photoshop. With this software, different texturising filters can be applied.

Foil blocking

Foil blocking is a variation on embossing using metalised film (foils) to create an interesting graphic product. The embossing stamp presses a pre-glued metalised foil onto the material using heat and pressure.

Foil blocking is used extensively on graphic products such as greetings cards and packaging for high-quality confectionary goods and can give added security to products like tickets when holographic foils are used.

Foil blocking

Coursework

Include details of the finish required for your product in the design specification and as part of the design development stage.

Activity

Create a poster with the heading 'Embossing' by collecting examples of graphic products that have been embossed.

Summary

★ Lamination is used to provide additional strength and protection.

★ Embossing provides a wide range of interesting visual effects.

★ Foil blocking uses metalised film to create interesting effects.

Industrial practices

Cutting, folding and creasing

In this chapter you will:

★ **learn the key principles of commercial die cutting**

★ **learn how press formes use press knives to cut and crease paper, board and thin plastic.**

Die cutting

One of the last stages in the production of graphic products is cutting, creasing and folding. It is at this stage that the packaging, which is already printed, is cut out of a large sheet on a machine called a die cutter.

Tabs, folds and cut outs used on packaging are produced on a machine called a die cutter

Die cutting is a process that uses steel rules – often referred to as press knives – to cut shapes from paper, board and other thin sheet materials. The basic principle of cutting is simple. Die cutting is similar to using a thin steel cutter for cutting out pastry shapes. Instead of a pastry cutter, a tool called a press forme is used to cut out and crease the shape required. In order to cut through the material, a huge force is required. In commercial die cutting a press that can apply 5–10 tonnes of pressure is used.

Press formes

Press formes are blocks of 12–15 mm plywood (used because it is strong and stable) with a series of steel knives placed into the grooves they have cut into its surface. The steel knives that are used for cutting have a V-shaped edge and are razor sharp. The blades used for creasing have a rounded edge, similar to a ballpoint pen.

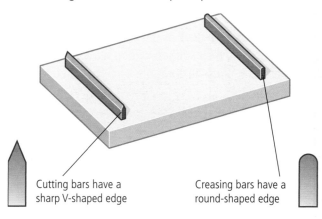

Cutting bars have a sharp V-shaped edge

Creasing bars have a round-shaped edge

Press formes (dies) are used for cutting out nets for packaging

The first stage in the production of press forme is the working drawing. The working drawing is the net (surface development) for the package that needs to be cut. The net for the supermarket bottle carrier below clearly shows all the cut and fold lines.

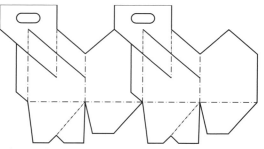

The working drawing shows the lines that need to be cut (solid lines) and the lines that need to be creased (dot-dash lines)

The working drawing is produced using CAD and is sent to the die cutting company as a computer file. This is usually either e-mailed or sent on a CD-ROM. Once the working drawing has been opened on the computer, the press forme maker can begin to work out the most efficient way of using the press knives to make the forme.

The net is then converted into a CAM file and the slots are machined into the plywood base.

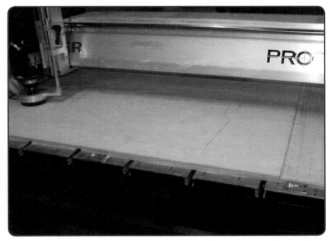

A machine called a router cuts the slots for the press knives into the plywood base

The cutting and creasing knives are carefully formed into the correct shape for the press forme. A special machine called a knife bender usually does this, but if the shape is relatively simple it can be produced by hand. Once cut and formed into shape, the cutting and creasing bars are carefully inserted into the plywood base.

The finished press forme has rubber blocks glued next to the press knives so that the waste material is pushed away from the press forme after cutting.

Finally, the formes are loaded onto a large press and the packages are pressed out.

Activity

Carefully unfold a carton and draw an accurate net showing all cut and fold lines. Indicate on the drawing the number of separate cutting and creasing bars that would be needed.

Summary

★ Die cutting is a process that uses special tools called press formes to cut out and crease packaging.

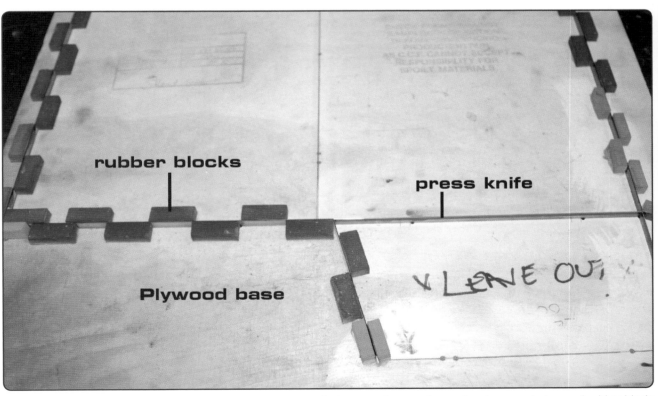

A close-up of a press forme showing press knives and rubber blocks

Industrial practices

Communication and marketing

Communication

During the design and manufacture of a product, a **concept model** is usually made. The purpose of this is to give the client, manufacturer and/or purchaser a good idea of what the final product will look like. At GCSE level, you may be involved in producing a fully working product (outcome), such as greetings cards and leaflets, or you may produce a realistic concept model such as a scale model of a shop interior.

Mock-ups and concept models

It is important to test ideas using **mock-ups** and concept models before a final design is submitted. These models can be of varying quality. Modelling allows the designer to experiment and test variations of an idea before more expensive work is done at the production stage.

Designers have three main methods for creating a realistic concept of a design idea:
- **3D modelling**: modelling materials like Styrofoam, card, foam board and sheet plastic can be cut, shaped and folded to the desired form.
- **2D modelling**: a pictorial drawing of a concept.
- Computer-generated concepts: use of CAD software like Pro/DESKTOP is an excellent method for quickly producing high-quality virtual products.

Marketing

Marketing is the way in which a product is brought to the attention of consumers and making them want to buy it. You can have a superb product but sell few items without a successful marketing strategy.

The purpose of marketing

There are three main functions of marketing:
- to sell the product to consumers
- to communicate information and messages

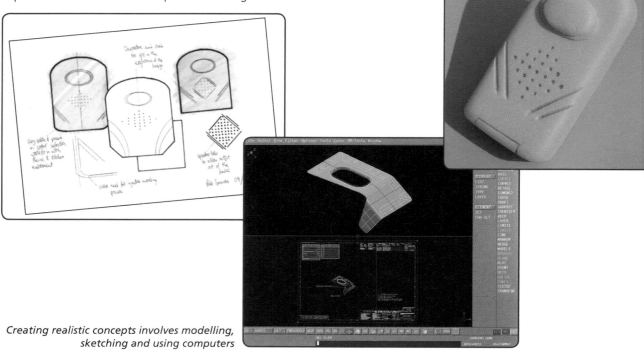

Creating realistic concepts involves modelling, sketching and using computers

- to present an image or idea that will persuade the consumer that they need the product or service advertised.

The marketing industry is now a diverse and important partner in the complex industries of design and manufacture. Any manufacturer who has developed a new product will contact a marketing agency to package and advertise it.

A marketing team consisting of product development and business executives will work with advertising, public relations and design consultants to create an image or identity for the new product or service. Designers will be commissioned to design and make any packaging that is required. This includes the actual container or wrapping and the graphics that appear on it.

Target marketing

When a new product is launched into a competitive market, it is usually aimed at a particular group of consumers, such as students, professional workers or children. The group will usually have been chosen by means of market research or by looking at various trends and fashions. Once the target market has been established, a strategy for advertising and displaying the product is devised.

Sometimes a product will have been designed from the first concept to attract a particular market. However, a totally new product or concept may need to be found a target market.

Companies are keen to spot a 'gap' in the market – a product that is not supplied by other manufacturers. Sometimes, the choice to the consumer is bewildering, thus the quality of marketing is even more important.

Coursework

It is essential that you produce 2D sketches and 3D models as part of your coursework. Models help you to visualise your ideas and are also useful for explaining your idea to a client.

Activity

Prepare an image board based on a chosen target group. Look at lifestyle, interests, activities, fashion, etc.

Summary

★ The purpose of an outcome is to communicate a concept.

★ Mock-ups and concept models are used to test ideas.

★ Target marketing is important when advertising a product.

Industrial practices

Case study: KitKat

In this chapter you will:

★ **learn how the elements of design are combined to make a classic graphic product.**

The red and white wrapper and the slogan 'Have a break – have a KitKat' are just two of the reasons why KitKat is Britain's favourite chocolate bar. In the overcrowded confectionary market, KitKat, with its strong graphic identity, stands head and shoulders above its rivals and has done so for many years.

The KitKat

From humble beginnings

KitKat was never originally called KitKat. The chocolate crisp bar was made and launched in London and the southeast of England in September 1935, and was called Rowntree's Chocolate Crisp. It only became KitKat in 1937, two years before the start of the Second World War.

KitKat was supposedly named after the KitKat Club, an eighteenth-century literary club. As the building had very low ceilings, it could only accommodate paintings that were short and wide. In the art world, these paintings were known as kats. It is believed that KitKat acquired its name from these paintings, which had to be snapped off to fit into the rooms with low ceilings. By 1937, KitKat was established as Rowntree's leading product, a position it has maintained ever since. During the Second World War, KitKat was viewed as a valuable wartime food and its advertising described the brand as 'What active people need'.

When KitKat was launched in September 1935, it cost 2d (around 1p in today's money). The first poster for KitKat appeared in 1951. Its first television advert was in 1957, with the memorable line 'Have a break – have a KitKat', and the first colour television advert was shown in 1969.

Building and maintaining success

Every second of the day, 47 KitKat bars are eaten around the world. KitKat is so popular that every five minutes enough KitKats are made to out-stack the Eiffel Tower and one day's production would stretch around the London Underground!

The logo is timeless and has been reproduced on countless products from clocks and watches to T-shirts and coffee mugs.

Merchandising using the KitKat brand helps to keep it at the forefront of people's minds

Features of the logo

One of the key features of KitKat's phenomenal success is its incredibly effective logo. The logo follows the easy-to-remember acronym SECRET. It is:

Simple
Easy to remember
Contrasting colours
Related to the company
Enlargeable and reducible
Transferable onto a range of different products

The KitKat logo has much in common with some of the world's top brands – Coca-Cola, Pepsi, Virgin and Oxo all use the red and white combination. Red is an aggressive colour and, when used with white, it really stands out. The use of a sans serif typeface ensures the impact of the brand and its simplicity. The product styling is maintained even when additional graphics are applied to the package. When diversifying into alternative Kit Kat products, the basic principles of the graphic design are maintained.

The basic graphic principles still apply when the KitKat design is changed

The words 'White Chocolate' are in a similar typeface to the main logo. The use of yellow as well as the main colour of red is a common colour combination (for example, McDonalds and Shell). Yellow is a primary colour and is submissive to the red. In order to maintain the dominance of the KitKat logo on the above wrapper where the colours are reversed, a common graphic technique of using a drop shadow is used – this gives the logo a 3D effect and makes it have enormous impact. The swirl added to the background symbolises the creamy taste of the chocolate. This demonstrates the importance of communication. Designers use visual symbols and images to persuade customers subtly and communicate messages to them.

Product differentiation

Successful brands like KitKat maintain their popularity (and profits for the company) by taking the basic product and making different varieties, thus appealing to different people (market sectors). The KitKat Chunky, White, Mint and other flavours are examples of product differentiation. Think about how other products use product differentiation to maximise sales.

 Activity

a Using the Internet, carry out research into one of the following classic graphic designs: Mars, Oxo, Coca-Cola, Brasso, Shell.

b Why is the product logo so successful?

Summary

★ The KitKat brand is an example of a graphic design classic, a design that has stood the test of time.

Industrial practices

In this chapter you will:

★ **learn how the elements of design are combined to make a classic graphic product.**

By studying designs considered to be classics, you can learn much about the elements of successful design.

What makes a classic design?

A classic design is one that stands the test of time; it does not change according to fashions or trends; and it combines image, quality and **innovation**. One such classic is the Toblerone brand.

The unmistakable shape of the Toblerone packaging is an example of unique branding. The product, which is sold throughout the world, not only has a distinctive name but is distinguished by its triangular peaks. For nearly a century this unmistakable chocolate bar has been a favourite for people across Europe and has helped to make Switzerland famous.

According to legend, the unusual shape may have been inspired by the most famous mountain in Switzerland, the Matterhorn. The logo on the packaging reflects this. Alternatively, it is rumoured that the shape may have been based on a more exotic theme. The creator of Toblerone, Theodore Tobler, regularly made business trips to Paris, where he visited the show at the Folies Bergères. As part of their stage act, the red and beige-clad dancers at the famous cabaret formed a human pyramid at the close of their number. Could this vision have inspired Tobler's triangular-shaped chocolate?

The elements of success

The font chosen for the packaging – a traditional serif typeface – gives the product a traditional feel. The typeface is emboldened with a drop shadow to make it really stand out. The light background not only communicates to the consumer a visual clue about the honey and nougat, it also provides clear constrast with the vivid red of the lettering. As with so many successful brands, red is a dominant factor. Notice the subtle use of gold around the letters. Gold

The cream and red packaging may have been chosen because Tobler loved Paris and was inspired by the costumes of the famous Folies Bergères dancers

is seen as a mark of quality. Products like Toblerone are saying through the use of gold that they are elite brands.

One other feature of the Toblerone packaging is the fact that the word Toblerone has been embossed. This adds to the quality feel of the product. Once again, the use of print finishing techniques, such as embossing, add to the image of quality. As customers, we feel confident buying such products because we subconsciously link them with quality.

One of the key issues for manufacturers of classic brands is to maintain product or brand loyalty. Making radical changes to a graphic image may confuse customers and place this loyalty in jeopardy.

Developing the brand image

Central to any successful product is the ability to communicate to customers the factors that make the product different. In recent years, Toblerone advertising has dramatised the difference between itself and other confectionary products.

In addition, the company has attempted to broaden its already substantial appeal by introducing bite-sized versions of the original bar.

Activities

1 What are the key features of design classics?

2 Why do manufacturers use print finishing effects such as embossing and foil blocking, even though they add to the cost of manufacture?

Summary

★ By studying designs considered to be classics, you can learn much about the elements of successful design.

A recent advertising image for Toblerone emphasised the uniqueness of its pyramid shape

1 The figure below shows a poster advertising a holiday resort. The poster is printed using the four process colours, C, M, Y and B. What do the letters C, M, Y and B mean? *(4 marks)*

2 Complete the spider diagram below by adding three more colour printing processes. *(3 marks)*

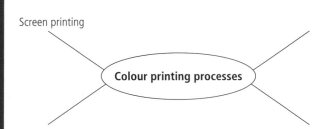

3 Look at the picture below, which shows a school dictionary cover.

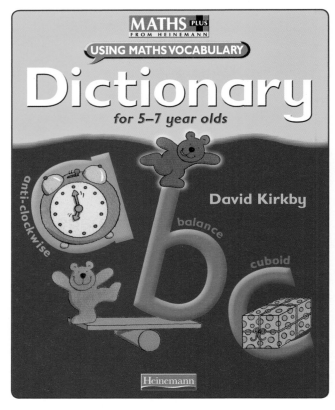

a Give two reasons why card is a suitable material for the dictionary cover. *(2 marks)*

b Name two finishes other than embossing for the dictionary cover. *(2 marks)*

4 a Printers' marks are applied to images during the pre-press stage of printing. Explain the purpose of the printers' marks. *(2 marks)*

b Draw the symbol for a registration mark. *(2 marks)*

5 In detail, describe the process of transferring original artwork onto a silk screen during screen process printing. Use notes and sketches where appropriate. *(6 marks)*

6 Digital printing is rapidly becoming a preferred commercial printing method for some manufacturers. Discuss the implications of the digital printing process to the manufacturer and/or consumer. *(6 marks)*

This section is designed to help guide you through the coursework section of your GCSE in graphic products, worth 60% of your final mark. The requirements are for you to design and manufacture a product prototype that could be made in quantity.

The main purpose of the project is to communicate a concept to a potential client. You can choose to create a single 3D product or a range of products that are in both 2D and 3D format. This could, for example, be a piece of packaging where the 2D element is the graphics printed on the package while the package construction is the 3D format. By choosing to create a number of products, you will increase the range and level of skills you demonstrate. As there are time limits for completing the work, it is important to choose a project that can be completed successfully on time – 40 hours for the full course or 20 hours for the short course. A typical design folder should contain approximately 15–20 sheets.

The coursework is broken down into two main sections for assessment:
★ designing
★ making.

Details of the assessment criteria can be found on pages 5–6.

When you set about completing your coursework, you will produce two things:
★ a project folio that is a record of your designing and planning skills
★ a piece of 3D practical work, which may include associated products in 2D and 3D format.

In a typical design folder, the design process is as follows:
★ description of situation, problem or theme
★ problem analysis

★ design brief
★ task analysis
★ preliminary research and analysis/results
★ product specification
★ design ideas and evaluation
★ design development
★ working drawings
★ manufacturing plan
★ a piece of 3D practical work, which may include associated products in 2D and 3D format
★ evaluation and testing.

However, you may find that the process is not always as straightforward as it may seem. Often you will have an idea or find a new piece of information that will make you rethink an earlier stage. This process is called feedback and is an important part of the design process. However, as long as you have a folder that is set out in a logical way, clearly showing how you have worked through the design process, the order of things is not too important.

Within each section there will be specific criteria for you to include and these are described in this section. Remember that regular communication with your teacher will be vital in helping you gain the best grade possible.

What's in this section?

★ **8.1** Situation/problem
★ **8.2** Writing the design brief
★ **8.3** Researching your ideas
★ **8.4** Product specification
★ **8.5** Design ideas
★ **8.6** Developing a design
★ **8.7** Plan for manufacture
★ **8.8** Evaluation and testing

In this part of your coursework you must:

A GRADE Use a wide variety of appropriate sources to gather relevant research information.

C GRADE Use a variety of appropriate sources to gather and order relevant research information.

Most designers set out to solve practical problems that arise out of life's situations. For example, many forms of packaging can be difficult to open. The materials and construction methods used make some packages strong, causing many consumers problems. It could be said that there is a need for a better form of packaging that satisfies the requirements of both the consumer and the manufacturer, ensuring a balance between usability and durability.

How do I decide what to do?

For your own work you may be given a variety of project outlines to choose from or be asked to investigate a situation where you can find a practical problem to solve yourself. The main thing is to find a project that can keep you interested for the whole time. If you decide on a project of your own choice, check the proposal first with your teacher to make sure you are going in the right direction. You also need to consider whether your school has the resources available to create your project.

To help define more clearly what you could do, it is often useful to analyse the situation of theme of study. A good way of doing this is to produce a mind map. This is where you write down as many related things about the situation you are studying. You may then find that you can focus on a more specific area where a design problem can be found. The analysis should direct you to the most suitable forms of research, which will ultimately provide the basis for your product specification.

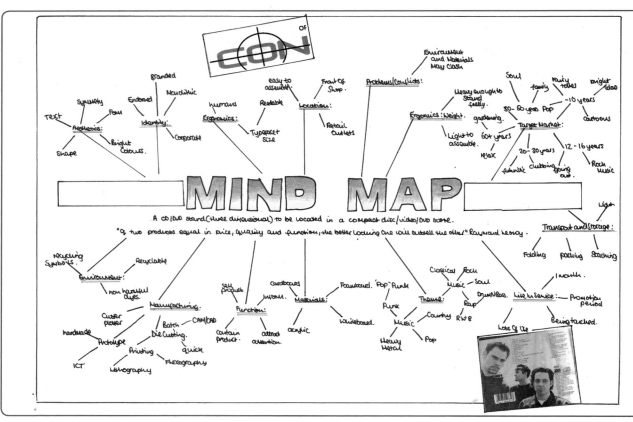

An example of a student's mind map

Writing the design brief

> **In this part of your coursework you must:**
> **A GRADE** Analyse the task and the research material logically, thoroughly and effectively.
> **C GRADE** Analyse the task and the research material.

Once you have analysed the situation or problem, it should be possible to write a short statement that clearly states your design intentions. This is called a design brief.

A design brief should be clear about you intend to do, but it should not be too detailed to curtail the designer's creative freedom. A good design brief could be as follows.

> **Design brief:** I am going to design and make a range of products to promote the music of a new rock band aimed at a teenage audience.

Notice that the brief states what is to be designed (in this case, promotional products) without actually stating what the products might be. It also states who the target market is. A brief like the example above allows a good range of ideas to be explored.

Now that you have a brief to guide you, the next stage is to analyse the task. This can be done in a similar way to the mind map on page 136, but now the analysis is more focused. A good way of breaking down the task into manageable pieces is to use the 5WH approach.

- **Who** is the range of users (target market) of the product? What age group are they? What gender are they are? What images would you associate them with?
- **What** has the product got to do? This is related to its function. What shape does it need to be? Do you need to use certain materials? What images, lettering, colours need to be used? What about quality vs. function?
- **Where** will the product be used or displayed? This is to do with its working environment. Will its position affect its design, weight, properties? Does it need to be weatherproof?
- **When** must the product be finished? What is the deadline? Try to finish your work before the deadline as this will allow time for you to get some feedback.
- **Why** is the product needed? Is there a similar alternative? Why must it be a particular size, shape or colour?
- **How** could the product be made? How much will it cost? How will the cost affect how it could be made? How will the product affect the environment? Will it be recyclable? How will you plan your time to ensure the deadline is met? How will you ensure a quality product?

Some of these questions will be easy to answer but some will be more difficult. To ensure you obtain the correct answers so that you can design the product, you must now carry out some research.

Doing your coursework project

The type of research you do depends on what information you need to find out. You should do no more than 2–3 pages of A3 in this section.

Research means finding out information, analysing it and then drawing conclusions about it that will help you with designing. Research is not just an exercise done at the start of a project. It takes place throughout the entire process as problems and questions arise. Every time you ask someone a question, browse the Internet or look up details in a book, you are carrying out research.

Research needs to be focused and relevant. Pages and pages of printouts from the Internet or a magazine will have little value and gain few marks unless it is absolutely necessary.

There are two main types of research:
- primary research
- secondary research.

Primary research

Primary research is sometimes called first-hand research and it is how you find out information that is not necessarily available already in a book or on the Internet. It helps you find out first-hand what the main problems and issues might be with your final prototype. It involves:
- visits and interviews
- conducting surveys/questionnaires or consumer trials
- carrying out product analysis of existing products
- taking photographs of a situation or environment relevant to your project theme.

In your project you need to show evidence of having compiled research from a number of sources. Two or three pieces of evidence from the above list would be fine. However, it is recommended that you carry out research into existing products and perhaps carry out a survey as a minimum.

Questionnaires

Questionnaires are a good source of primary information but they need to be designed and targeted carefully. You need to choose a sample of people who reflect the likely users of the product. Questionnaires are useful for finding out user preferences (what people like or dislike).

Care must be taken when writing a questionnaire so that you find out exactly what information you need. Here are some general tips:
- Use tick boxes where possible.
- Avoid open questions that require a long answer.
- Only ask questions that will give you useful information.
- Use closed questions, which give people a choice of options to select.
- Use visuals – useful for finding out what style or colours people like.

The information collected from a questionnaire will have little value unless it is analysed so that conclusions can be drawn from it about your design work. Use the following questions to analyse your results:
- What are the main things that users prefer?
- How will the results affect your design specification?
- Does the question help you to make decisions about things like the colour, shape, cost, size, weight and function of the product you will make?

Pages 32–33 give more information on how to present data.

Analysing existing products

Much can be learnt by analysing existing products that are similar in nature to what you intend to make, such as use of materials, construction methods and manufacturing procedures. Look at the following examples of product analysis sheets taken from a student's GCSE coursework.

The handwritten student sheet reads:

RESEARCH Product Analysis Leaflets

- MY LEAFLET IS ADVERTISING GO KARTING
- ITS AIMED AT CHILDREN OVER 10 AND ADULTS
- THERE ARE PHOTO OF PEOPLE ON THE GO KARTS + THEM PEOPLE SMILING IN ALL THEIR KARTING GEAR TO SHOW THEY ARE HAVING FUN.
- THE TEXT STYLE IS SERIF + THEY HAVE USED BLACK MOUNTING TO MAKE IT STAND OUT OUT. I DONT THINK THE STYLE RELATES TO THE THEME BUT YOU NOTICE IT COS IT STANDOUT.
- A HARMONISING COLOUR SCHEME HAS BEEN USED. RED, ORANGE + YELLOW FOR THE BORDER + GREEN IN THE MIDDLE.
- SEVERAL IMPORTANT PIECES OF INFORMATION ARE HIGHLIGHTED THROUGHOUT THE LEAFLET + THE THE PRICE LIST IS LAID OUT IN A WAY THE ITS EASY TO READ.
- I THINK THE LEAFLET MAY HAVE BEEN MANUFACTURED BY FLEXOGRAPHY. WHAT CYLINDERS ROTATE TO PRINT ONTO PAPER OR CARD.
- FLEXOGRAPHY IS USED FOR PACKAGING CARTOONS OF POINT OF SALE MATERIAL + IS OFTEN USED FOR LONG RUNS AT LOW COSTS.

GCSE Graphic Products

A student's product analysis sheet

To be successful at product analysis, you need to consider the following.

- Analyse against a set of criteria (see the product analysis checklist below).
- The analysis results lead you towards writing a specification of your own.
- Ensure the analysis is well presented and easy to understand.

It is a good idea to use a prompt sheet to help you when analysing a product. Use the product analysis checklist on page 140 as a guide. Answer the questions in turn, but remember that, depending on the type of product, some questions will have more relevance than others – decide what is relevant to your project outcome.

Secondary research

Secondary research is easier to carry out than primary research. It involves looking at work produced by other people. Things like reviews in books or on the Internet are a good source. Secondary sources include:

- magazines
- CD-ROMS
- the Internet
- experts in their field.

As part of your GCSE course, you must try to include ICT within the coursework. Carrying out research on a computer is a good way of doing this. Websites on the Internet can provide a wealth of information. However, take care not to spend too long doing web searches as time can easily be wasted. Know what you need to find out before you log on, and make sure your research is relevant to your design brief. ICT is also good for helping with your coursework presentation, particularly if this is an area you find difficult. It is useful for presenting simple statistical data from your questionnaire results using charts and graphs.

Now that you have completed some research and analysed it, you are ready to move on to writing a product specification.

Content/layout

- What information is conveyed? Is it instructional or promotional?
- Does it function as it was designed to do?
- Is the information communicated overt (obvious) or covert (hidden)? Sometimes a message is deliberately hidden to make people think more deeply about a product or issue. Why is this?
- How are the graphical images, headings and information laid out on the product? Some products, like promotional leaflets, have clear layout rules – with the front page being about grabbing attention and general information while the inside has specific details about the activity or item being promoted.
- Do some of the graphic layouts lead your eye towards a message or entice you to turn the page?

Target market

- What is the market for the product or service? How can you tell?
- Who uses it?
- What clues can you find in the text, colours and graphics to show the target market?
- Are different styles used for different age groups?

Aesthetics

- What makes the product look good? How has the designer used colour, symmetry, balance and typography?

Ergonomics

This is about how easy a product is to use and what features a designer includes to make this happen.

- Are specific sizes taken into account? For example, a design for a leaflet holder will need to have details on the sizes of leaflet.
- Is the type (lettering) easy to read?
- Has the designer taken into account how the user might use the product?

Materials

Materials are important, not only for structural properties but because different materials can affect how a design will look and feel.

- What materials have been used and why? Do they relate to the purpose?
- What properties do the materials used need? For example, are they tough, stiff, flexible, lightweight, easy to print on?
- How does the cost of the product affect the material choice?
- Does the manufacturing method affect the chosen material?

Typography

- What style of text is used (serif, sans serif, stylised, script)?
- Does the style and size of lettering affect the impact of the graphic?
- What type of text layout has been used (left justified, centred, right justified)?
- Has ICT been used?

Product specification

The next stage in the design process is to use the information you have found out and bring it all together to produce a product specification. This is a list of features (design criteria) that your final project must have. This should be no more than 1–2 pages of A3.

Writing the design specification is one of the most important parts of the design process. The best specifications use sub-headings for key features and bullet points for specific criteria.

Use the following sub-headings as the basis for your own specification. Answer the questions as they apply to your project. Remember that some aspects will be more relevant than others – it all depends on what you are making. Remember to concentrate on the product not the process.

- Timescale for production: What is the project deadline?
- Function: What is the design meant to do? What is its purpose?
- Performance: How will it satisfy the function? Where will it be used?
- Target market: What age group are you aiming at? What is their social type – student, young professional, etc.? Who will use your product?
- Aesthetics: How will colour, line, shape, form, texture, pattern, layout and tone contribute to the visual appeal of your design?
- Ergonomics: What effect should your design have on its human user? What anthropometric data do you need to use in your design? How will the size of the product be determined?

- Materials: Which materials will be suitable to use and why? What material properties are you looking for (weatherproof, easy to clean, lightweight, cheap, recyclable, easy to print on, reflective, matt, scratch resistant)?
- Manufacture/quantity: How will your design be produced – printing methods, pressing, embossing, laser cutting, batch or one-off production, use of CNC machinery or manually-operated equipment, consideration to environment, ethical issues, economical use of materials, etc.
- Maintenance: How will the design be kept in good working order? What features will the design have to make this easy?
- Reliability: How can you ensure the product will work each time it is used?
- Life in service: How long do you intend the product to last?
- Cost: Is there a budget? What will be the selling price? What will the product cost to manufacture in large quantities? How many items need to be sold to break even?
- Weight: Light or heavy – does it matter?
- Safety: What safety factors will you need to consider? What standards are there?
- Quality: What quality factors will you need to consider? Quality control/quality assurance.
- Environmental and other issues: How will you ensure your product minimises any potential damage to the environment? Think about the 3Rs: reduce, recycle and reuse. How will you ensure your design takes into account any moral, social and cultural issues? These often produce conflicts, which can be very difficult to resolve.

The next stage is to get creative!

Design ideas

Design ideas are the first thoughts we have about a solution to a problem. Sometimes, before designers put pencil to paper, they produce a mood/image board.

Mood/image boards

These are a collection of images related to the theme of your design and the type of person who might use your product. They can be collections of colours, textures and extracts from related magazines.

A way of creating a mood/image board is to put related themes together as a kind of collage. This will give you some visual starting points to help you with your design.

A mood board

Initial ideas

For your coursework you must produce a wide range (at least 6 or 8 different ideas) of possible solutions. It is important to make sure that each idea is different. Designers often call these first ideas 'rough visuals' and they do not need to be a work of art in terms of quality. What you will be graded on is how many ideas you can come up with and how accurately they match your design specification. See pages 16–17 on sketching to help you do this.

It is a good idea to break down your ideas into separate areas. For example, when doing a project based on promotion or corporate identity, there may be common design elements such as a logo, a style of lettering or a colour scheme that could be used on a variety of products. Therefore, you could produce ideas for each element – logo, lettering, colour scheme – and then combine them together to form a complete product. In this way, the product develops naturally and helps you to come up with a wider variety of solutions. This is also how you will be asked to produce ideas in the examination.

What ideas do I use?

When you have created a range of ideas, you need to start making decisions about which designs to use and which to reject. These decisions need to be shown on your design page by annotating them with evaluative comments. You should evaluate your ideas against your design specification. Ask yourself the following questions:

- What are the best features?
- What are the poorest features?
- How could it be made?
- What materials could be used and why would I choose them?
- How well do the ideas match the whole specification?

One of the key features of the GCSE project is that the product you design should be able to be manufactured in quantities greater than one. This means you must think about how a commercial company might manufacture your product.

Communicating your ideas

You need to be able to communicate your ideas to others. This is an important design skill and is known as the visual language of design. At initial design stage, you should always:
- use initial or quick ideas (in 3D where appropriate) and annotate them clearly
- ignore tiny details – these will come later
- think in simple terms, then add complexity later
- produce a wide range of ideas
- magnify an area to show detail
- make your pages look compact and lively.

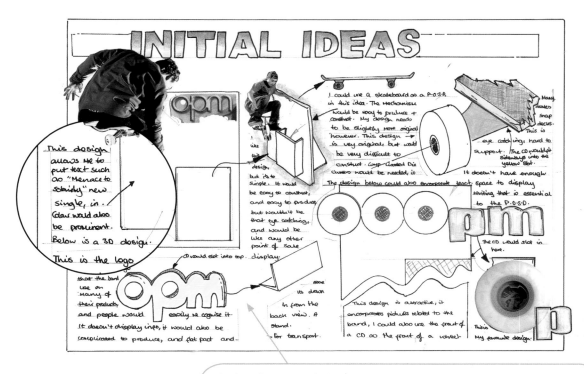

The key features of this A grade project are:

- A wide range of drawing and rendering, both 2D and 3D.
- Clear annotation – writing against the side of each idea that not only evaluates them but also relates the idea back to the specification
- Good use of ICT mixed with pencil and pen sketches.

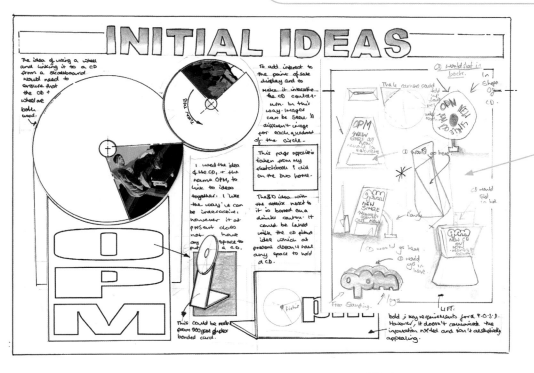

This sheet shows that ideas don't have to be 'pretty' to be valuable

Initial ideas

Developing a design

In this part of your coursework you must:

A GRADE

1 Use one or more of your proposals and relevant knowledge of techniques, manufacturing and working characteristics to develop a detailed and coherent design solution.
2 Provide evidence that you have considered and taken account of relevant issues, industrial practices and systems and control.

C GRADE

1 Use your proposals and relevant knowledge to develop a detailed design solution that satisfies the specification.
2 Provide evidence of having considered relevant issues, industrial practices and systems and control.

Developing your original ideas

The development stage is an important part of your coursework and is worth a substantial number of marks. It is part of the design process where you add more detail to your chosen ideas in an effort to improve them or to develop a better solution. This is where you can combine ideas and start to use methods other than drawing and sketching to help define and refine the solution. These other methods include modelling by making a mock-up using a material like card or by computer modelling using a CAD program like Adobe Photoshop or CorelDRAW.

Two-dimensional designs like logos or lettering can be developed quickly using CAD, but hand-drawn/rendered ideas can also be used. Whichever method you use, it is important to show how the original idea has been altered, modified, added to or transformed into a more workable and likely solution. A series of sketches can help to show this.

Use the checklist below to make sure you have developed your design.

1 Have you produced a sequence of drawings (freehand and/or CAD-generated) showing the development of your design from initial sketch to fully detailed plans? These should include:
   a concept sketches showing subtle changes to the design as it progresses. Modify your basic idea as you go along. Try combining ideas, change colours, a variety of layouts, typography, proportion, sizes, etc. This provides an excellent opportunity to use a CAD package, perhaps after scanning in your basic idea.
   b details about possible methods of manufacture. Remember that you have to consider manufacturing in quantities greater than one – think about quality control, jigs, fixtures and templates.
   c details about sizes and tolerances for each part of design.
   d details about surface textures/finishes, such as embossing.
   e details about any scientific principles being used, such as smart materials and mechanisms to create movement.
2 Have you carried out enough research? You may need to find out information about colours, materials and production methods.
3 Have you made simple mock-ups?
4 Have you evaluated your ideas against your specification? Does your product do what you said it would?

Look at the examples opposite of students' GCSE work to see how development has occurred in both 2D and 3D designs.

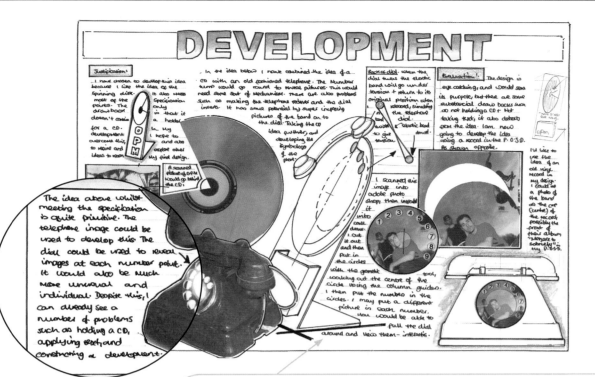

DEVELOPMENT

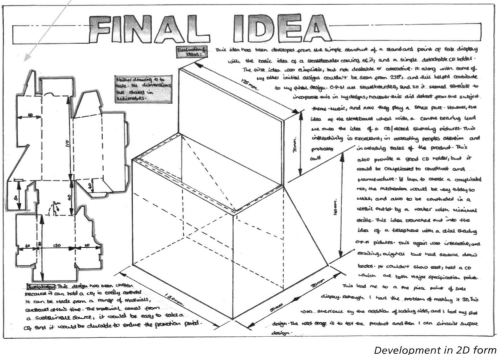

FINAL IDEA

The designer constantly evaluates ideas and seeks to refine them as he goes. ICT is mixed with pen and pencil sketched. It shows a good range of drawing techniques. The development sheets read like a book and it is possible to trace the idea back through each stage as it logically develops.

Development in 2D form

Towards manufacture

It is important to test ideas using mock-ups. Paper, card or any other appropriate material can be used for these. If these models are too bulky to include in your design folder, take photos of them. Never throw away any work, 2D or 3D, which may be relevant. Mock-ups are also good for assessing how a product could be made. Each feature can be evaluated and an appropriate manufacturing method chosen.

Commercial manufacture

The key consideration when thinking about how to design your product with manufacture in mind is how to achieve consistency in quality. Remember that your product needs to be designed for manufacture in numbers greater than one. This can be achieved in a number of ways. Where appropriate, use processes and techniques similar to those found in industry, like the following.

- Templates: these are devices that help to speed up a process, like marking out a shape.
- Stencils: these are similar to templates, but rather than being used as marking-out tools, they are used to mask off areas that do not require any colour or texture. They are good for doing repeat pattern, like a simple wallpaper print.
- Colour bars: these are used in the print industry (see pages 112–113). Printers apply a bar of colour to the edge of a piece of print so that checks can be made to ensure the colour quality is maintained. You can do this easily on a computer CAD package, and it is a good way of demonstrating your understanding of how 'real world' quality control is achieved.
- CAM: use computer-controlled machinery to manufacture your model, i.e. a 3D model can be machined in plastic or a development of a packaging net can be cut out on a plotter/cutter.

Working drawings

Now that you have developed and tested a design that best fits the requirements of your specification, it is time to produce detailed drawings. These should include information on:

- the type of material to be used
- the dimensions: give the size of each feature
- construction: how it will be put together
- graphic details: visual imagery
- typography: lettering styles
- quality: the standard required.

2D products – master artwork

As a starting point, if you have a common element like a logo or lettering style that could be repeated onto both 2D and 3D products – for example, a poster and point-of-sale display – it is a good idea to produce a master artwork. This master copy of the graphic you intend to use can be produced in whatever medium you think is best. The graphic should be made to a suitable size, but keep to standard sizes like A5, A4 or A3. This gives you the best chance of achieving quality in detail. Once completed, add crop marks, registration marks and colour bars (see pages 112–113). It is then possible to enlarge, reduce, scan or copy the master artwork onto or into the graphic of another product.

Once you have a master artwork, you need to produce detailed drawings of any other graphical work that is to be used.

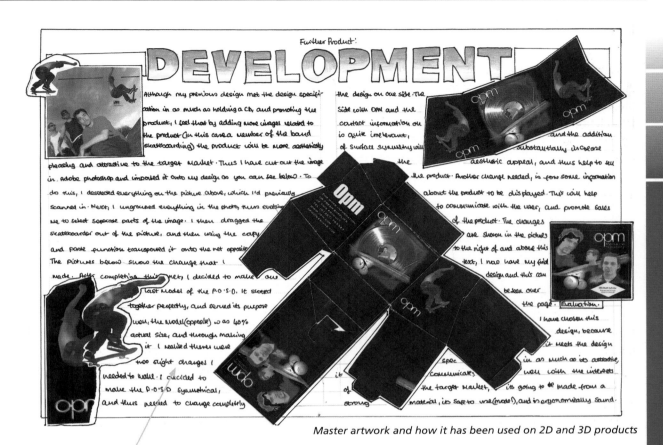

Master artwork and how it has been used on 2D and 3D products

This development section shows excellent use of CAD software package to produce a very high quality product.

The annotatation describes the process but more importantly evaluates the ideas it develops

3D products

Three-dimensional products need to have drawings that show exact dimensions, tolerances (see page 107) and construction details. Suitable drawing methods can be:

- orthographic projections: third angle
- isometric drawing: good for visualisation
- perspective drawing: good for showing the product in its working environment.

See pages 26–28 for more information on the above drawing methods.

A successful set of working drawings should be able to be used by a manufacturer to make the product to the standard you require.

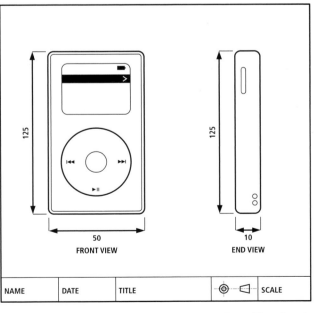

A working drawing

Doing your coursework project

Plan for manufacture

Flow diagrams and charts

Before manufacture can begin, you need to plan the order in which you will make your product; show which processes, tools and equipment will be used and where; and explain why and how production decisions will be made. This activity can be made easier by breaking down what needs to be done into stages. The following stages will help you to produce a flow chart (see pages 82–83), which is a simple way of showing a production sequence.

Stage 1

Make a list of all the activities (marking out, cutting, printing, rendering, etc.) you need to do to make each component of your product. Do not worry about putting them in the correct order – just make sure you have left nothing out. A good method is to write down each activity on a piece of card.

Stage 2

Decide on the order that these activities need to come. If you have written down each stage on a piece of card, you can shuffle these around until you think you have them in the correct order. For example, marking out a shape onto a piece of plastic needs to come before it can be cut out.

Stage 3

Once you have a list giving the order of activities, it is possible to add things like the timings for each stage, the tools needed and the processes used.

Stage 4

Now that all the relevant detail is in place, you can produce a more formal plan on how to manufacture your product. It is possible to use a variety of methods:

- Flow charts with feedback routes – see pages 82–83. Flow charts are useful for communicating the main plan of action and sequence of operations, but they can become cumbersome and complex. The main problem is that they lack the detailed information needed for production.
- Sequence illustrations – see page 84. Sequence illustrations are good at showing assembly information as they convey graphically what needs to be done and, for many people, a visual image is easier to understand.
- Schematic maps – see pages 84–85. Schematic maps can be useful as they simplify a plan into a straight-line route, making it easy to see what stage you are at.

All the above methods could be used to plan your manufacturing activities, but all have certain limitations on their own. To solve this problem, production schedules are used and, together with the above methods, a detailed and thorough plan can be achieved.

Production schedules

Production schedules include much more detail and complement the information given in, for example, a flow chart. They also include quality assurance and quality control procedures to ensure that the objective of producing a high-quality product is achieved.

Producing a production schedule

Production schedules are normally pre-printed in the form of a grid are provided as a standard template in a piece of software like Microsoft Excel. In industry, a production planning engineer decides how a product will be made and fills in the form. A production controller then makes sure the schedule is followed. For your coursework, you will take on the roles of both the production planning engineer and the production controller. For your production schedule, you need to include the following headings in the form of a grid:

- Stage or task: a brief description of the process to be carried out.

- Tools, materials and processes: this should list the resources needed for each stage, such as cutting equipment, card, plastics.
- Accuracy required: this states acceptable tolerances (see page 107).
- Quality assurance: a statement about how you are going to ensure mistakes will be avoided.
- Quality control: how you are going to check the accuracy and quality of the product using visual checks, use of a gauge, etc.
- Alternative methods: alternative ways of making if things go wrong, perhaps using different materials or processes.
- Health and safety: the hazards, if any, involved in the process/stage.
- Time needed: an accurate forecast for how long each stage will take to complete.

It may be that you have a number of products to make. This could mean producing a separate schedule for each product, or a longer single one, with each product listed separately to ensure clarity.

Any schedule must set realistic deadlines and identify critical points in the process where decisions have to be taken and where any quality control checks need to be made. This is where a flow chart used in combination is useful. Aim to include both a flow chart and a production schedule in your plan.

Remember to take into account that you are manufacturing your product in school and this may result in additional pressures, such as the length of lessons or the restricted use of resources (for example, CAD/CAM equipment may not be available for use by more than a few students at a time). Use your experience of making previous products to help produce your schedule.

PRODUCTION

N.B. Once this process is complete the point of Sale Display would be flat packed and transported to the retail outlets.

Once in the retail outlets it will be constructed by the workers. Instructions will be included but no construction skills are needed to make.

Schedule:

Task:	Tools, equipment and/or process.	Time Needed:	Quality Control:	Health and safety:	Back up Plan:
Take floppy disk to printers. Including image.	Floppy disk.	Varied, depending on distance to printers.	Keep disc in protection case to eliminate damage.	Make another floppy copy of disk, in case of loss or damage.	No eating or drinking whilst near disk. (This task and health and safety should be swapped for this example.)
Load computer, and select file, open design - jpeg. Load lithography machine with whiteboard.	Pentium 3 processor fujitsu personal computer.	2-5 minutes depending on condition of computer and whether it has been switched off properly previously.	Has the computer run up properly? And is it in the correct mode.	No eating or drinking by the computer, and ensure regular breaks happen.	Use different computer, and make sure another is available before to compensate for the broken one.
Check print preview, and correct printer to screen, and lithography plate machine.	Lithography machine, and Pentium 3 processor fujitsu personal computer.	10 minutes.	Ensure plates are correctly positioned, and design is correctly aligned on sheet. (A3)	No eating or drinking. Be careful when using lithography machine as there is a danger of fingers trapped.	Print design on to card using A3 printer and turn off lithography machine.
Set computer to separate ink in lithography machine.	Lithography machine, Pentium 3 processor, and ink.	10 minutes.	Ensure colours are separated properly.	Be careful colours don't mix.	Bring back up ink, or print design on to A3 whiteboard using colour printer.
Set the computer to start the lithography process.	Lithography machine, Pentium 3 processor and ink.	2 minutes.	Ensure everything's working and switched on properly.	Make sure ink doesn't cross, and nothing is in the machine.	Print out using Pentium 3 processor computer, using colour laser printer.
Remove whiteboard from lithography machine. Apply lacquer using rollers, placing it under an ultra-violet light to dry.	Lacquer (which can be dried by ultra violet light. Industrial rollers. Ultra violet light. Sunglasses.	15 minutes.	Apply lacquer carefully, placing a piece of paper or such under whiteboard to ensure lacquer doesn't run.	Wear sunglasses, to make sure that your eyes aren't injured by the intensive ultra-violet light.	Apply oil based varnish that can be dried normally, or put through laminating machine.
dried, leave out to dry under ultraviolet light.	Ultraviolet light, sunglasses.		Place something to the side of it, or put it in a slot to keep it still.	Wear sunglasses to protect eyes.	Bring two backup ultraviolet lights that you could use if one breaks.
Turn on diecutting machine, which will stamp out the design (cut out). This will also fold or crease the design, the equivalent of scoring, and feed batch through.	Die Cutter.	2 minutes.	Wear safety goggles and gloves. To ensure particles don't dog machine, and ensure design is put into correct slot. Ensure die cutter is sharp enough.	Wear safety goggles and gloves to protect your hands and eyes from sharp bits in the die cutting machine.	Cut design out using metal safety rule, knife and cutting board. Score along all the lines where the P.O.S.D will need to folded using blunt knife and metal rule.

A student's example of a production schedule

Doing your coursework project

Evaluation and testing

In this part of your coursework you must:

A GRADE Test, objectively evaluate and effectively modify your work throughout the process as appropriate and in detailed comparison to your specification.

C GRADE Test, evaluate and modify your work throughout the process and compared to your specification.

An evaluation is a series of questions about how well your design has met the requirements of your specification. There are two main types of evaluative methods: formative evaluation and summative evaluation.

Formative evaluation

Evaluation does not take place only at the end of a project; it is an ongoing process throughout the whole project. A formative evaluation occurs every time you make a decision or judgement about your work, such as when annotating your design ideas.

Summative evaluation

At the end of your project, you must complete a detailed analysis of your final outcome. This is called a summative evaluation and it must relate directly to your specification. It judges your final product against each element in your specification. A detailed specification is therefore important, otherwise it is impossible to carry out a meaningful evaluation because there are no criteria to make judgements against.

Aim to cover the following points during formative and summative evaluation.

- Consider each point on your product specification. Have you done what you said you would do? Use the same sub-headings to make it easy for the examiner to follow the logic of your work.
- Include sketches and photos to show how you could improve the product – a diary of manufacture should help here.
- Write in the third person – do not say things like 'I think...'
- Say what could be improved and what effect any improvements will have on the function and performance of the product.
- Get other people's views – in particular, your client or a member of the product's target market.
- Test your product in action if you can. Does it function and perform as required? Observe and record people's reactions to it. Do they like it? Try to obtain data: did they find it easy to use, how many times was it used in a given time span, was it used more or less than other similar products?
- Do not write your evaluation as a diary of what you did – it is not an evaluation of how you managed the project, only of how well the product meets your specification.
- Remember that all designs can be improved and most will need some small adjustments, even if they are successful.

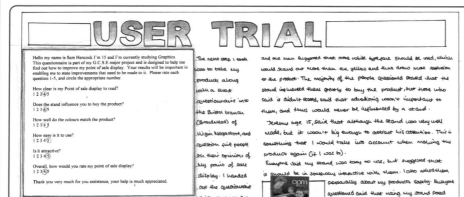

An evaluation carried out by a student

This section focus on the main elements of the written exam. It provides sensible advice and guidance on how to go about preparing for and taking the written exam.

What's in this section?

★ **9.1**   Exam requirements

★ **9.2**   Exam preparation

★ **9.3**   Getting the marks!

9.1 Exam requirements

In this chapter you will:
★ learn about the requirements of the written exam paper
★ learn how to make the best use of the preparation sheet.

The facts

- Students perform much better in coursework than they do in exams – on average, about two grades higher.
- Poor exam technique often limits students' achievement.
- Some students have a limited understanding of technical vocabulary – they use simple language rather than the actual names for tools and processes.
- Exams test similar things to coursework but some students seem to be unable to transfer these skills.
- Product analysis is arguably one of the most important skills required for success in exams – therefore, learning facts alone is insufficient preparation for success.

It is easy to think that once the coursework is finished, it is the end of your course. However, the examination is worth 40% of the total marks for the GCSE. You will need to spend a good deal of time analysing previous exam papers, revising all the theory in this book and researching the background information provided for you by the examination board.

Requirements of the exam

Your teacher will have entered you into either the higher-tier examination paper or the foundation paper – make sure you know which one you are taking. The higher-tier paper is targeted at GCSE grades A–D. The foundation paper is targeted at grades C–G.

The lowest possible grade that can be awarded on the higher paper is a D (although, under certain conditions, the exam board can award an E). This means that if you get less than a D on the higher paper, you will automatically receive a U grade. The highest possible grade that can be awarded on the foundation paper is a C, so even if you get a mark of 100%, you will only achieve a grade C.

Exam preparation sheet

On or about 1 March in the year of your exam, you will receive the exam preparation sheet from the examination board. The theme of the examination changes every year. This sheet is designed to help you to focus your research on the topics that form the basis of the examination paper.

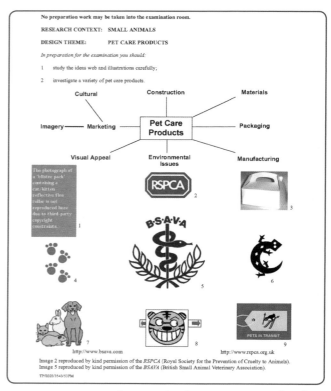

An example of an exam preparation sheet

This preparation sheet gives you important clues and should be analysed carefully. It not only provides you with the theme for the examination, it gives you the key content areas that you will be examined on.

Using the preparation sheet

Using the exam preparation sheet example above, the key areas for research into the main theme of pet care products are given in the diagram opposite. These are marketing, visual appeal, environmental issues, manufacturing, packaging, materials and construction. Materials are always a key area – in this example, ask yourself about the different materials used in pet care products and why they are used.

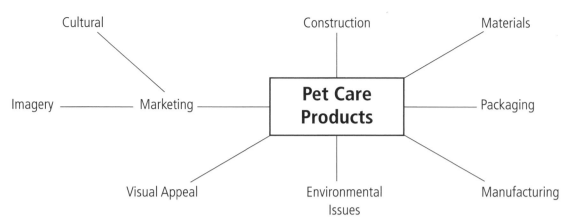

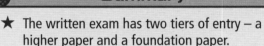

Key research areas

These key areas are given as a basis for analysing pet care products and applying your knowledge. This means you have to take a fact, such as 'the process of vacuum forming is used for blister packaging', and then state why and how it is used for the packaging of certain pet care products. The best way of doing this is by looking at as many pet care products as you can and analysing them.

Clues are given to you on the preparation sheet about where to find information. In this case, they are given in the form of logos.

- Use the Internet to find out information about these organisations. Focus your research on their products, not on what they do. For each product, use the research areas from the preparation sheet as a basis for your analysis.
- Write to or e-mail the organisations, asking for information. However, many companies may fail to reply so do not rely on this as a main source of your information.
- Visit pet shops and superstores.
- Collect leaflets, take digital photos (ask for permission from the shop owner) and, where possible, buy a selection of products – all these should be analysed.
- Compare last year's preparation sheet with the actual exam paper to see how the key areas of research translated into questions.

Summary

★ The written exam has two tiers of entry – a higher paper and a foundation paper.

★ The exam is based on a theme, which is given to you well in advance of the exam in the form of a preparation sheet.

★ The questions on the exam paper require you to apply the knowledge you have to a specific product related to the theme.

★ The theme of the exam changes each year.

Preparing for the exam

Exam preparation

In this chapter you will:

★ **learn how to produce a revision plan and revise successfully.**

The key to success in all exams is to have a plan for revision. Start early and do not learn something only once. Revisit it many times, practise the skills needed (for example, orthographic projections, drawing and rendering) and do not spend too long revising in one go – little and often is the key because after 10–15 minutes your brain is less effective at taking in information. Drink plenty of water because this oxygenates the brain.

Preparing a revision plan

Write the plan on paper, noting all critical dates and times. Be reasonable and build in some free time. Make sure the following are identified:

- all exam dates
- coursework deadlines
- study leave
- family occasions, birthdays, holidays and trips
- some time for relaxation and exercise – you will need to be fit for your exams.

Divide the remaining time between all your subjects. When allocating time to each subject, take into account the following factors.

- How well did you do in the mock exam? This will help you identify areas you are strong or weak in.
- When is the date of each exam?
- What is your preferred method of learning? Do not allocate yourself time that you will not use effectively. Variety created by 'little and often' or 'topic by topic' may be more effective.
- Use colour-coded blocks for each subject to give you a clearer indication of how much time you have allocated time to each subject.
- Buy some Post-it notes and write things on them that you find difficult to remember. Stick them in prominent places around your bedroom such as on your mirror, so you are constantly reminded of them.

- Do not be afraid to alter your plans as circumstances change, but try to stick to your revision plan as closely as possible.

Revision methods

Revision requires you to make the most of your notes, textbooks, coursework folders and practice exam questions. There are many ways to help you remember important things about graphics. The following list may help.

- Do not simply read your notes or a textbook. Highlight key points as you go, using indexing tabs to locate important aspects and to help create revision cards for later, quicker run-throughs.
- Sometimes work with a friend or willing relative. They can test you as you go and prompt you where necessary.
- Practise questions under strict time conditions, as many exams can turn into 'time trials' if you are not used to working at the required speed.
- Revise in comfortable, suitable surroundings. Music may help but a television is more likely to distract.
- Be organised and tidy. Time wasted searching for material in a pile on the floor or on your desk can never be recovered.
- Practise examination skills too. Your exam will last for two hours, so you must be able to think and write neatly for that long. This will be especially important for practical skills such as sketching, drawing and rendering.

Summary

★ Success in the examination requires you to go about your revision in a planned and careful way – never leave things to chance.

★ Make a realistic, detailed revision plan, allowing for all your subjects.

★ Do not rely on just learning facts – this is not enough for success in graphic products.

9.3 Getting the marks!

> **In this chapter you will:**
> ★ learn how to tackle the exam paper with confidence by developing an understanding of the different types of questions and responses required.

Taking the exam

It might sound obvious, but the first thing to do is to read the front cover of the exam paper very carefully. Use the following points as a checklist.

- Are you in the correct tier?
- Have you got all the equipment you need?

Version 1.1

Surname		Other Names			Leave blank
Centre Number		Candidate Number			
Candidate Signature					

General Certificate of Secondary Education
Summer 2003

**DESIGN AND TECHNOLOGY
GRAPHIC PRODUCTS**

HIGHER TIER

Thursday 12 June 2003

In addition to this paper you will require:
- a pen, pencil, ruler, eraser, pencil sharpener and coloured pencils.
- Marker pens and 45/60 degree set squares may also be used.

Time allowed for the whole exam: 2 hours

Instructions
- Use blue or black ink or ball-point pen.
- Fill in the boxes at the top of this page.
- Answer **all** questions in the spaces provided.
- Detach the blue sheet from the back of the examination paper to use in between the sheets to prevent ink bleeding through to the next sheet.
- Do **not** hand in the blue sheet at the end of the examination.

Information
- The maximum mark for this paper is 125.
- Mark allocations are shown in brackets.
- Wherever calculations are needed you should show your working.
- All dimensions are given in millimetres unless otherwise stated.
- You are reminded of the need for good English and clear presentation.

Advice
Answer the questions in the order given.

For Examiner's Use			
Number	Mark	Number	Mark
1			
2			
3			
4			
5			
6			
7			
8			
Total (Column 1)	→		
Total (Column 2)	→		
TOTAL			
Examiner's Initials			

Make sure you read these notes – they are very important and failure to follow instructions may lead to problems

Students often fail to get the marks they deserve in an exam because of weak exam technique. Exam technique means the skills you show when completing the exam paper in the way examiners expect.

The design question

At the start of the question, you will usually be given the design criteria that will relate closely to the preparation sheet. You will have used design criteria or an outline specification in your coursework to guide you with your ideas. You must read these criteria carefully.

You will probably be asked to:
- produce two design ideas to choose from which meet these design criteria – to gain the full marks they must be significantly different and well annotated
- choose one of the two ideas as your final product
- detail how your final product will be made.

Therefore, the question will relate to the design idea you choose, so make sure you have not drawn something you are not familiar with.

As part of your preparation for the exam, you need to practise for this design question by practising designing products.

Tackling the exam with confidence

First, you need to work out how much time to spend on each question. The total number of marks on both the higher-tier paper and the foundation paper are 125. The length of the full-course exam is two hours (120 minutes). This equates roughly to one mark per minute. By using this time guide, you should never fail to complete the paper. The exam paper always gives you an estimated time allowance for each question.

Make sure the responses you give correspond to the verb used in the question. The most common verbs used in the exam paper are name, give, explain, describe, develop and evaluate. Each of these verbs requires a specific type of response.

Name is usually a one-mark question because it requires a one-word answer that is simply the recall of a fact. An example is given on the next page.

Preparing for the exam

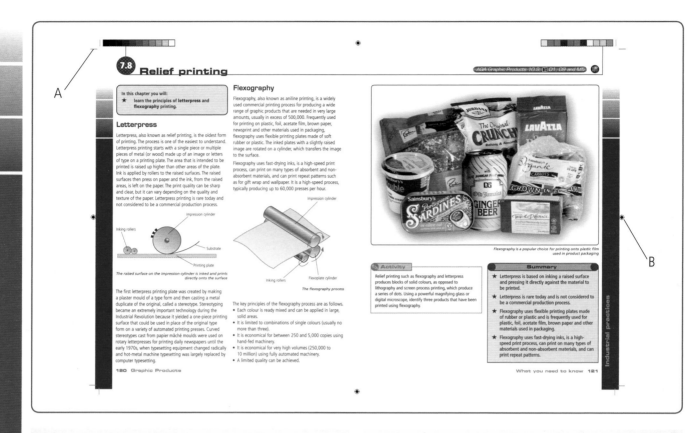

The page shows a textbook spread for section 7.8 Relief printing, pages 120–121 of Graphic Products.

Question

Look at the illustration above. Name the two printers' marks labelled A and B.

Printers' mark A   ....

(1 mark)

Printers' mark B   ....

(1 mark)

Give requires a short sentence as an answer. This type of question is usually used with a qualifier – a reason or example. This is a higher order response and requires some understanding.

Exam Hint
Look the amount of space allocated for the answer to 'give' questions on the exam paper – it is rarely more than two lines, meaning a short answer is required.

Question

Give one reason why card is a suitable material for a dictionary cover.

(2 marks)

Giving a reason means you have to answer the question fully. A suitable answer to the question above might be 'Card is strong compared to paper'. One-word answers are unacceptable.

Explain requires you to recall a fact and then apply it to a particular situation.

Exam Hint
An example of an 'explain' answer is 'PVC is a suitable thermoplastic for vacuum forming (recall) because it is rigid and lightweight (application).'

Questions

1 A label on some products has the message 'SAFETEY FIRST'. The ink used is a smart material. Explain the term 'smart material'.

(3 marks)

2 Explain how a thermochromic ink works.

(2 marks)

Describe requires you to correctly describe a process, usually using sketches and notes. This type of question requires recall of facts but it must be the right facts for the identified process. You might need to draw a flow chart, but as a minimum you need to get each stage of the process in the correct order.

Question

Describe, with sketches and notes, the process of vacuum forming.

(5 marks)

Develop and *evaluate* are used with questions that require you to design a solution. Develop means improve upon an initial idea and evaluate requires you to compare something against a list of criteria such as a design specification and to come to a decision.

Question

Using the specification develop ideas for a typeface (font) for the charity's name, Petsafe.

(6marks)

Finally, think before you write. Try to answer the question in context. You will probably have experienced the situation set by the question when working on your coursework. Imagine you were back in the design studio or workshop. What would you do and/or what would you use to do it? Then read the question again and answer it.

Summary

★ Always read the front cover of the exam paper before you begin.

★ Students fail to get the marks they deserve because of weak exam technique.

★ The length of the exam is two hours. This equates to roughly one mark per minute.

★ Answer the questions!

Glossary

A

Analyse/analysis To ask questions using the 5WH approach – who, what, why, when, which and how.

B

Batch production A method of production where a number of components are made all at once. Repeated batches are sometimes made over a longer period of time.

British Standards Institute (BSI) The national standards body for the UK. It provides a set of standards that all products must meet in order to be considered safe to use.

C

CMYK Cyan, magenta, yellow and black. The four process colours used in printing.

Coated A surface finish, like varnish, applied to a material.

Computer-aided design (CAD) Use of a computer programme to design a product.

Computer-aided manufacture (CAM) Use of a computer programme to manufacture a product.

D

Densitometer An electronic instrument used to measure the quantitative colours or density of colour in printing.

Desktop publishing (DTP) The term used within ICT for the layout of text and graphics using dedicated software.

Die cutter A tool similar to a pastry cutter that uses thin blades to press down and cut and/or crease irregular shapes in card.

E

Embossing A process that raises the surface of a material using a press or stamp. Normally used to give an interesting visual affect.

F

Flexography A printing process that uses flexible printing plates, usually rubber or plastic. Used predominantly for packaging.

Flow chart A chart using symbols to show the sequence of a process.

Function The purpose of a product, i.e. what it does.

G

Graphic identity When an organisation uses visual symbols or logos to separate them from other companies.

I

Information and Communication Technology (ICT) The name given to the study and use of computers, the Internet and associated communication devices such as mobile phone technologies and digital television.

Isometric A pictorial (3D) drawing method based up lines drawn at 30° to the horizontal.

L

Laminating A process where two or more layers of material are bonded together, like a plastic coating on card packaging.

Letterpress The original relief method of printing, whereby a raised image or letter is primed with ink before paper is pressed onto it.

Lithography A printing process that produces an image from a flat dampened plate using greasy ink, based on the principle that water and oil do not mix.

M

Marketing The selling of a service or product to a customer.

Mould A hollow or convex shape used for shaping a material, like in vacuum forming.

N

Net The 2D shape or development of a 3D product in sheet form.

O

One-off production When a product is made by one person.

P

Perspective A form of drawing in 3D using vanishing points along a horizontal axis or eye line.

Planned obsolescence Designing and manufacturing products in the knowledge that they will be replaced shortly.

Plotter cutter A computer-controlled output device for producing accurate lines or cuts on card or paper.

Point-of-sale display (POSD) Graphic products that are used to advertise a product in a shop, often mounted on a counter or a shelf.

Prototype A pre-production version of a product, used to check whether it meets requirements.

Q

Quality assurance A policy or procedure written to ensure that a product reaches the customer to the correct specification.

Quality control Systems put in place to check the quality of the product during manufacture, e.g. gauges, visual checks.

S

Scale of production The type of production, i.e. batch, mass, one-off.

Scanner An input device used to import images into a computer for DTP.

Screen printing A low-volume method of printing onto different surfaces using templates, a wire mesh and ink.

Specification A set of clearly indicated criteria that the final solution must meet.

T

Third-angle projection A 2D drawing method commonly used for making drawings.

Three-dimensional (3D) modelling A method of communicating a design in three dimensions, either by using suitable resistant materials such as card, wood, MDF and clay or by using computer software to show virtual 3D images.

Two-dimensional (2D) modelling This usually involves making either a card, paper or thin plastic model of a product or a computer-generated model using a program such as Pro/DESKTOP.

Typeface A type design (text style) including variations like italic and bold.

U

Uncoated Refers to paper used in books, catalogues, etc. in a range of finishes such as rough or smooth.

Index